STRUCTURES
with
MATERIALS

Steve Rich

Head of Design, Weatherhead High School

Stanley Thornes (Publishers) Ltd

Text © Steve Rich 1991

First published in 1991 by:
Stanley Thornes (Publishers) Ltd
Old Station Drive
Leckhampton
CHELTENHAM GL53 0DN
England

British Library Cataloguing in Publication Data
Rich, Steve
    Structures with materials. – (GCSE technology)
    I. Title   II. Series
    624.1

ISBN 0-7487-0151-6

Acknowledgements

The author and publishers wish to acknowledge with thanks the following sources of photographs:

Associated Press p. 35; British Cement Association p. 37 (bottom); Building Research Establishment, Crown Copyright p. 38; City Repro Photo Unit, Newcastle upon Tyne p. 33 (bottom); Dartmoor National Park Authority p. 33 (top); Early Learning Centre p. 52; Ford Motor Company p. 71 (top); Grove Worldwide p. 3; Ironbridge Gorge Museum Trust p. 37 (top); John Markham Collection, English Nature p. 7; Loctite UK p. 58; Mansell Collection p. 36; National Monuments Record for Wales p. 34; New Civil Engineer p. 85; Norfolk County Council Library and Information Service p. 87; RAPRA Technology Ltd p. 46; RS Components Ltd p. 43 (bottom); Anne Russell pp. 48, 63; Sussex Express and County Herald p. 4 (bottom); Thomas Mercer Ltd p. 43 (top); Caroline Thompson pp. 4 (top), 70, 86; Stewart Thompson p. 59; Timber Research and Development Association p. 71 (bottom); The Welding Institute p. 60.

Cover photo: Leslie Garland Picture Library

The publishers have made every effort to trace the copyright holders, but where they have failed to do so they will be pleased to make the necessary arrangements at the first opportunity.

Diagrammatic artwork by Mark Dunn
Cartoons by Phil Payter Graphics
Typeset in 11/12½ Italia by Tech-Set, Gateshead, Tyne & Wear
Printed and bound in Great Britain at The Bath Press, Avon

Contents

Preface

This book is designed to be a self-contained course that will be 'user friendly' to both student and teacher. It contains a series of graded design problems that can be used sequentially or independently. This allows flexibility in the use of the material.

The book takes into account the varied requirements of the National Curriculum through the medium of high technology. It has been tried and tested as teaching and reference material for students preparing for GCSE technology examinations (equivalent to Key Stage 4).

The author recognises that not all schools have the same level of equipment and therefore the development of a specification for each design brief has been omitted. It is envisaged that this can be developed by the students, who need to be aware of what equipment is available to them.

Chapter 13 is a research section, providing more detailed information on a variety of topics to which students can refer to help them develop their own designs. The topics are arranged in alphabetical order.

All diagrams in this book have been drawn to British Standards where appropriate.

Steve Rich
1991

CHAPTER 1

Students' guide to the book

Every chapter in this book contains information on a particular aspect of structures or materials, together with a theoretical and practical activity to help you to develop your understanding.

When doing practical work you should be aware that the tools and artifacts you make can be dangerous. We recommend that you read Chapter 2 *Safety* before starting on your practical work.

As you read through this book you will find that each section can be used on its own to explore a particular topic or idea or it can be combined with the others to give you a complete course in structures and materials.

To avoid confusing detail, the *analysis/research* sections do not include all the work needed to fully design and install a complete solution to the design problems. You will need to add more information if you are to model the solutions accurately.

You may not need to read every chapter or all the parts of the *Research* section. Seek your teacher's advice on which sections of this book are most important in terms of your examination syllabus. If you do read and use all of this book then your project work will be helped by having a wider understanding of structures and the use of materials in them.

Good luck!

Safety

In a controlled situation structures are safe. Many of the solutions to problems described in this book can be fabricated from common materials. This will require the use of simple tools and machinery. If they are used incorrectly they can present a serious hazard to the user.

To ensure that you work safely here are some simple guidelines:

1) **Dress sensibly for the workplace.** If you are using hazardous materials or equipment protect yourself in the correct way. Wear goggles and an apron as a minimum level of protection.

2) **Tools with sharp edges or powerful clamping actions must be treated with care.**

3) **On/Off switches must be obvious and within easy reach of the operator.**

4) **When using machinery it is important that moving parts are guarded.**

5) **If you are hurt or injured get help straight away.**

6) **If in doubt about safety ask your teacher.**

Personal safety is an issue that everyone should take seriously. Always remember *machines don't suffer the consequences of accident - people do!*

What is a structure?

We are not always aware of structures. Which of the objects drawn below do you think has a structure? Which do you think do *not* have a structure?

It is probably easiest to identify an object as a structure if it:

a) Carries a load:

b) Does not collapse in normal circumstances:

c) Holds itself together even under load.

Frame structure

Carcass structure

From these guidelines it can be argued that every object shown so far has a structure.

Structures can occur naturally, for example, a tree, or be fabricated, for example, a bicycle. There are two basic types of structure used by nature and man. They are the **frame**, made from several parts joined together, and the **carcass** or **shell** where the outside layer of the structure holds the whole object together.

Natural structures

Most animals have skeletons. But this structure, which is supporting the body, may be on the inside or the outside of the animal. An internal skeleton is called an endoskeleton, and an external skeleton is called an exoskeleton.

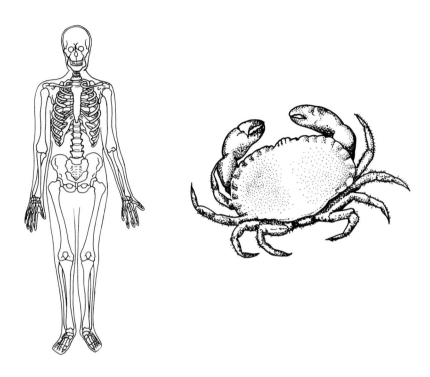

A human has an endo-skeleton, but a crab has an exoskeleton

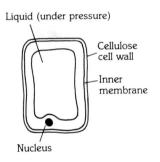

A typical plant cell

Plants also have a supporting structure. It is the plant's cells which support the living plant.

In a healthy plant the cells form a strong structure. The liquid pressure inside each cell (**hydrostatic pressure**) helps to keep the shape firm and able to resist outside forces such as gravity. If the plant loses fluids the cells start to empty. As the cells collapse the plant's structure starts to weaken, causing the plant to wilt.

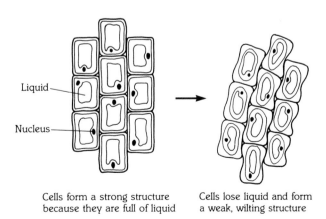

Cells form a strong structure because they are full of liquid

Cells lose liquid and form a weak, wilting structure

Some plants also use woody cell walls as structural material. The cells are reinforced by lignin in the walls and do not rely as much on their liquid content for support.

Fabricated structures

Many man-made structures reflect natural forms. An artificial structure that relies upon internal pressure to keep its shape is a car tyre. The compressed air inside the tyre helps it to keep its shape when it is loaded. The compressed air spreads the load around the whole tyre, keeping the surface in tension.

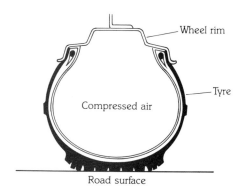

However, humans have developed many structures that do not resemble natural forms. Some of the factors that have influenced the development of man-made structures are:

- the size of the structure(s)
- the availability and type of materials
- the function of the structure
- the tools available to make the structure
- the technology and know-how of the builders
- the available labour force
- environmental considerations – will it damage the environment or improve it?
- the cost of the materials and labour.

The following illustrations show some common types of fabricated structures.

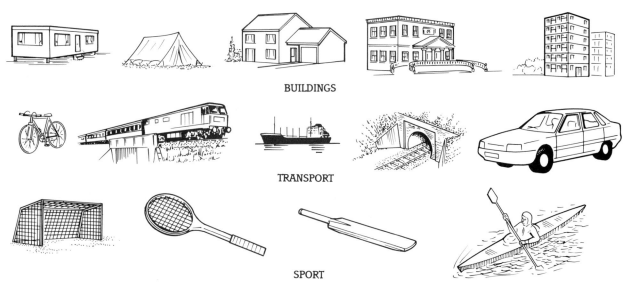

BUILDINGS

TRANSPORT

SPORT

FURNITURE

CONSTRUCTION

ENERGY

SAFETY/PROTECTION

Don't forget that animals and insects can fabricate structures as well as humans!

Wasps construct an elaborate nest from chewed-up wood

The language of structures

Forces

Structures have to withstand the loads and forces acting upon them. When a load is applied to a structure, it produces a number of forces inside the structure that resist the load. These are called **internal forces.** There are two main kinds of load.

Static loads
These are loads on the structure that do not change, for example the weight of the bricks or stone used to make a bridge, or the materials used in making a road surface.

Dynamic loads
Loads on a structure that change are called dynamic loads. These can be caused by traffic crossing a bridge or by the flow of water under it (hydrostatic pressure).

A car crossing a bridge exerts forces upon it. The forces are from the outside of the bridge structure and are called **external forces.**

To support the car on the bridge the structure must oppose the forces exerted by the car. These forces act within the structure of the bridge and are **internal forces.**

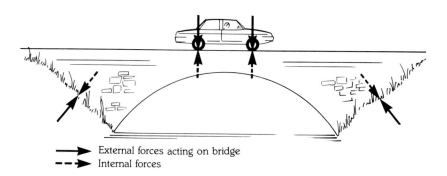

→ External forces acting on bridge
--→ Internal forces

If the external forces cannot be balanced by the internal forces, the structure will be moved and/or caused to break.

Sir Isaac Newton (1642-1727) studied forces and their effect on objects. He proposed two physical laws to describe how they behaved. (Newton's First and Third Laws of Motion can be found in the research section, Chapter 13.)

Tension forces

The cable holding the lamp is in **tension.** Each end is being *pulled* in opposite directions.

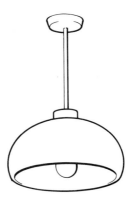

When a force acts to stretch a material it is called a **tensile force.**

Compression forces

In effect the stand is squashed between the loudspeaker and the ground. Each end is being *pushed* in opposite directions. The two forces put the stand in **compression.** Forces that produce compression are called **compressive forces.**

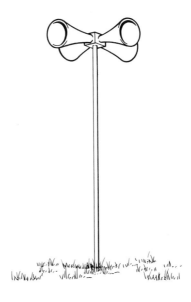

Shearing

Shearing forces occur when compressive forces are not acting along the same line. Scissors cut by using this type of force.

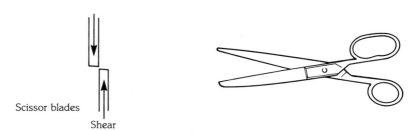

Scissor blades

Shear

Turning forces

When a bolt is fastened into a threaded hole it is normally gripped with a spanner. The bolt is tightened with **turning forces.**

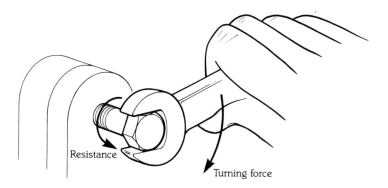

The tightening force is resisted as the bolt is fully tightened, putting the bolt under **torsion.** The turning effect produced by the spanner is called **torque.**

Bending forces

When a beam is held at both ends and loaded in the middle it is bent downwards. This type of loading causes a **bending** force to be applied to the beam.

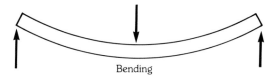

This bent shape can also be caused by compression acting on the ends of the beam.

The neutral axis

When a beam is bent upwards, its top surface is stretched and in tension. The underside of the beam is squeezed and in compression. Where one type of force changes to the other in the middle of the bar there is an area that is not in tension or compression. This zone is called the **neutral axis.**

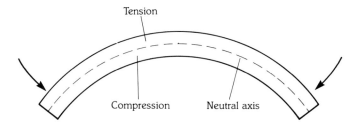

If the beam is bent in the opposite direction the tension and compression forces in the bar are reversed.

Sagging

If a beam is subjected to large compression forces it will be forced to shorten. If it springs downwards the beam is **'sagging'**.

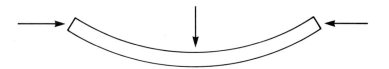

Note: The sagging is caused by the compression forces only, not by any load in the middle of the bar.

Hogging

If a beam springs upwards when subjected to large compression forces it is said to be **'hogging'**.

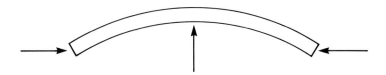

Note: The 'hogging' is caused by the compression forces only, not by any external forces acting on the middle of the bar.

Structural elements

Structures can be analysed to see what the different parts do. This enables a designer to check that all the parts are doing the correct job and to find out if there are any parts that are not carrying a load. Special names are given to the different parts depending on the job that they are doing.

Struts

A **strut** is the name given to material supporting a compressive load. The main column of this drum stand is in compression and is therefore called a strut:

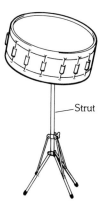

11

Ties

Structural material in tension is called a **tie.** The cable supporting this lamp is in tension, therefore it is a tie.

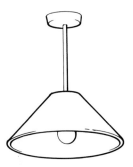

Beams

Beams lie horizontally and are supported in one or more places. They have to carry a load, or loads, along their length. There are two main sorts of beam: the **simple beam,** and the **cantilever beam,** which is a beam supported at one end only.

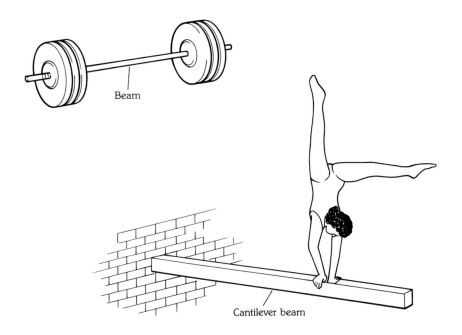

Beam

Cantilever beam

Brackets

Brackets are used to give support to beams. They take a compressive load and are a type of strut.

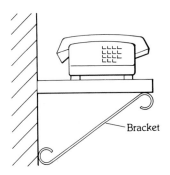

Bracket

Stays

Stays are used to support struts or beams. They are in tension and are a type of tie.

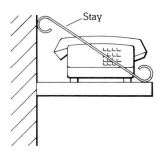

Redundant members

When there is a part of a structure that does not have to support a load it is said to be a **redundant member** (not doing anything to support the structure).

In the diagram below the stay and the bracket are both doing the same job. Either one of them could be removed and the structure would work just as well. The item removed could be called a redundant member.

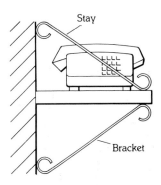

Redundant members are not always removed from a structure. They may not have a structural function but their purpose may be to make the structure look better. Also, the use of 'redundant members' may enable the structure to be made lighter because they add additional strength and support.

Triangulation

The shelf can be supported by either a stay or bracket. The shape made by the shelf, support and wall is a triangle, whether it is using a stay or a bracket.

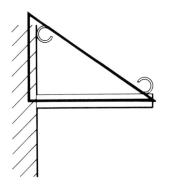 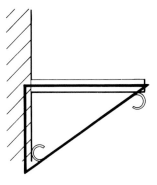

13

Draw a simple line diagram of the seat you are sitting on. Label each of the parts of the structure so that it can be easily identified (Bow's notation, see the research section, may help you). Using the simple flow chart below, complete a structural analysis of the seat.

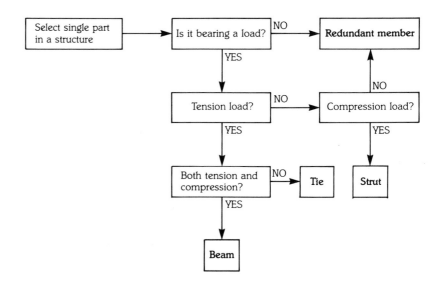

You should be able to identify the function of each part in structural terms, i.e. strut, tie, beam or redundant member.

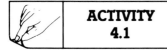

Beams can react in rather strange ways when forces are applied to their ends.

Hold a thin 300 mm plastic ruler horizontally between the palms of your hands and press firmly inwards to compress the ruler.

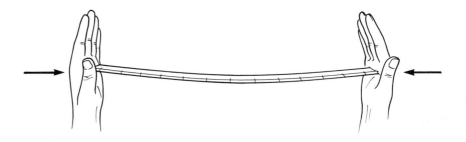

1) If you press hard enough the ruler will suddenly change shape. Transfer the curved profile of the ruler onto a piece of paper. Add arrows showing the compressing forces to your diagram and an arrow to show the direction in which the centre of the ruler moved.

2) Repeat the experiment and try to make the ruler move in the opposite way. Trace the profile of the ruler again. Add arrows showing the compressing forces to your diagram and an arrow to show the direction in which the centre of the ruler moved.

3) Describe the performance of the ruler under compression. Add these terms to your drawings.

CHAPTER 5

Equilibrium

Design problem

Mules have been used to carry loads for many centuries. They can go where wheeled transport cannot pass. One of the problems with them is that they are very stubborn and reluctant animals.

In the situation above, the ol' Prospector is having difficulty in persuading his mule to move. A balanced state has been reached where neither the Prospector nor the mule can move. Their efforts cancel each other out and balance. There is a special term that describes this state: equilibrium.

Any system or object is in a state of **equilibrium** when it is not moving and any forces acting on it cancel each other out.

Design brief

What can be done to help the ol' Prospector and 'persuade' the mule to move?

Analysis/research

Forces have size and direction. They can be represented in drawings by arrows: the length of the arrow can show the size of the force and the direction of the arrow shows the direction in which the force is acting.

A single force will try to move an object in the direction in which the force is acting.

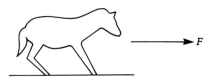

If two or more forces act on the object in the same direction, they have the same effect as one force the size of all the forces added together:

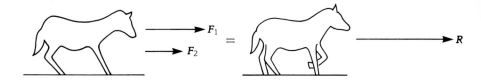

The total force, R, is called the **resultant** force.

Here, $R = F_1 + F_2$.

If you want to prevent the force from moving the object, you must apply another force to the object. It must be the same size as the first force, but act in the opposite direction. This force is called the **equilibrant.**

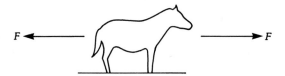

The object stays still: it is in equilibrium.

To change the state of equilibrium a force must be added or removed.

Design solution 1

Evaluation

This solution could work, the state of equilibrium has been changed by the addition of a force. The ol' Prospector would be making progress. But the disadvantage is that this solution requires a large amount of force from those involved. As there is no one available to help the ol' Prospector, this solution cannot be used.

Design solution 2

Evaluation

This solution could work: the state of equilibrium has been changed by the removal of a force. The ol' Prospector would be making progress. Much less force is involved.

The disadvantages are that this solution requires some equipment, but if these can be found this would seem to be the best solution.

Copy the drawings of Design solutions 1 and 2. Underneath them draw labelled arrows representing the different forces in each case.

On each of your drawings show which forces are the *resultant* forces and which forces are the balancing *equilibrant* forces.

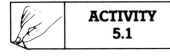

1) Investigate a variety of situations that rely on equilibrium for success.
2) Discuss how the forces are balanced in the following situations.

Shelter

Throughout history people have sought to improve their environment. Seeking warmth and shelter is something we do instinctively. Natural structures that can provide good shelter are rare, but people have used them since the dawn of history.

Artificial shelters start with simple use of the landscape, using the shade of a tree or a hedge as a windbreak. A simple wall running east to west can provide shelter from the sun in summer and a less windy zone to the south in winter. On a summer day the rocks will absorb the heat of the sun, giving it out again in the evening.

To stay warmer and drier some insulation from the ground is needed. This can be done by using a layer of stone, wood or dried plants. A lean-to roof will help to keep off rain and snow. This is an example of a **frame** structure.

Solid walls would increase the shelter provided by the structure, and a fire in front of the opening would warm the occupants by direct heat and heat reflected from the walls. Further improvements could be added by the occupants. The walls form a **shell** structure.

The development of primitive buildings may have started in this way. Most societies have developed shelters to meet their particular needs. The styles of structure have depended on many factors and include:

- the lifestyle of the people
- the environment and climate
- the function that it will be used for
- the materials and expertise available to make it
- the labour force available to make it
- the need for a temporary or permanent structure.

Shelters are space-enclosing structures that have to be supported. They will all need foundations and either a frame or shell construction.

 **ASSIGNMENT 6.1**

Research the topics of foundations, frame and shell (carcass) construction. Use a range of sources of information.

Design problem

A group of pupils is taking the Duke of Edinburgh Gold Awards. For their expedition they will need some form of shelter that they can carry themselves. There are no tents available.

Design brief

Design a simple, portable shelter for one person to use on a short expedition.

Analysis/research

To provide a suitable solution to this problem it is necessary to analyse the problem, breaking it down into a list of what the solution must be or do if it is to be successful. This list is called a **specification.**

ASSIGNMENT 6.2

1) Develop your own specification for the solution. The ideas below might help.

For how many nights will the shelter be used?
What are worst weather conditions that will have to be withstood?
How many people will need to fit inside the shelter?
Where will the personal kit and cooking facilities go?
Will the shelter be tall enough to stand, kneel, sit or lie down in?
What will need to be kept inside the shelter, and what will need to be kept outside?
How will it be assembled/carried/packed?
How will the structure be kept secure and stable?
Are there any ground conditions that should not be used to set the shelter up on?
What costs will be involved in producing it?
Will it harm the environment in any way?
What materials will you use for the frame, the covering and for protection from the ground?

2) When you have drawn up your specification, use it to evaluate the design solution below.

Design solution

The frame is a simple one, two king posts pushed into the ground. Each end is linked by a ridge pole. All poles are made from aluminium tube. The ridge pole is tied onto the king posts. A heavy-duty polythene sheet is draped over the ridge and held down on either side by large stones or boulders.

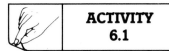

ACTIVITY 6.1

1) Keep a record of what you have learned about the strengths and weaknesses of the design above in terms of your specification.

2) Produce your own design for a shelter. You may find the information on 'triangulation' in Chapter 4 and on reinforcing materials in the research section (Chapter 13) useful.

3) If you can construct your design, test and evaluate it.

Playing with forces

Structures are normally seen as being stable, non-moving objects. This is misleading, because in order to be stable a structure has to respond to every force that is applied to it.

The following examples should help you to understand some of the effects that forces can produce.

Design problem

A television programme relies on the competitors completing physical and mental tasks against the clock. Because the first series of programmes is coming to an end a new set of tasks is required for the next series. Models of new ideas are required for consideration by the programme producer.

Design brief

Design a new game that requires the use of forces to achieve a prize.

Analysis/research

The following conditions have been laid down by the television company:

1) The game must be interesting and require intelligence, ability or skill to be completed.

2) The game must be safe.

3) There must be a penalty for failure (i.e. no prize will be gained).

4) The competitors must only be able to extract a prize if they have correctly completed the task within the allotted time.

Combining forces

Remember: Weights are measured in kilograms, but forces are measured in newtons.

Calculating the results of several forces acting on an object can be done mathematically, but it is easier to work out an answer by using a scale drawing. As forces have size (or magnitude) and direction, they can be represented in a drawing by using arrows. The length of the arrow can represent the size of the force and the arrow's angle or direction shows the direction in which the force is acting. These force arrows are called **force vectors.**

A single force will try to move an object in the direction in which the force is acting, as we saw in Chapter 5. The effect of two or more forces acting on an object is more difficult to predict. When they all act in the same direction we can just add them up (see Chapter 5).

Resolving two forces into one force in complicated situations makes them easier to understand.

Space diagrams

If a force or forces are acting on an object their effect can be represented graphically in a **space diagram.** A space diagram of force vectors acting on a point looks like this:

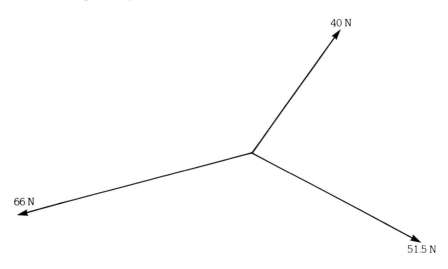

Space diagrams allow combined forces to be worked out by drawing rather than calculation.

Force diagrams

A **force diagram** is made by drawing to scale all the force vectors acting on a structure so that they are connected 'head to tail' and follow each other round. If the structure is in equilibrium and stable the force vectors will make a closed shape (called a polygon).

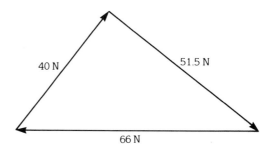

If the polygon is open, the missing vector represents the missing force that will bring the structure back into equilibrium. The direction and size of the arrow will represent the force to scale.

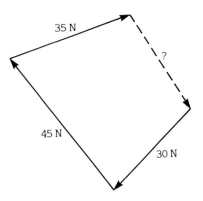

Parallelogram of forces

When the forces are at an angle to each other the resultant is worked out using a scale drawing of the force vectors called the **parallelogram of forces.**

If there are two forces acting on the same point, O, this is how the combined effect of the two forces is worked out by using force vectors. In this example we shall call the forces 'Force left' (F_l) and 'Force right' (F_r). They act at an angle of 90° to each other.

A suitable scale is chosen and the force vectors are drawn to represent the direction and magnitude of the forces.

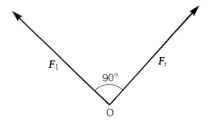

Two lines are then drawn parallel to F_l and F_r which cross at a point (R).

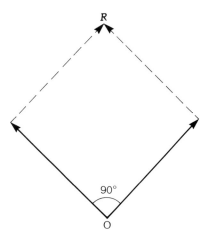

A line is then drawn from point O to the point R. This force vector is called the **resultant** of the original two forces.

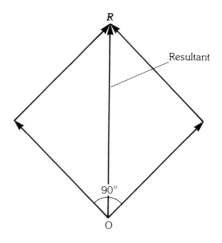

Triangle of forces

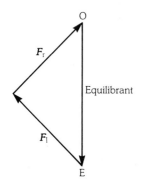

To balance the two original forces and bring them into equilibrium the **equilibrant** force needs to be found.

The two force vectors F_r and F_l are drawn (in either order) from a starting point O. A force vector drawn from the end of the second vector E to the start point O will be the equilibrant.

This produces a **triangle of forces.** Note that the force vector arrows all flow around the triangle in the same direction.

The equilibrant is the same size as the resultant but acts in the opposite direction to it.

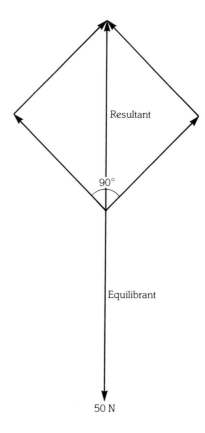

Component forces

To calculate the values of two component forces that make up a known resultant force use this method.

1) Draw the resultant force vector to a suitable scale.
2) Draw lines at the angles of the known component forces.
3) Construct a parallelogram of forces.

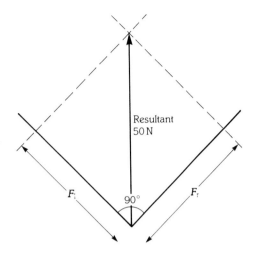

Resultant
50 N

F_i

90°

F_r

4) Use the scale of the drawing to find values for the component forces.

Design solution 1

A simple frame is attached to the outside of a tall tower to support a pulley. A rope runs over the pulley and through a hole in the tower wall.

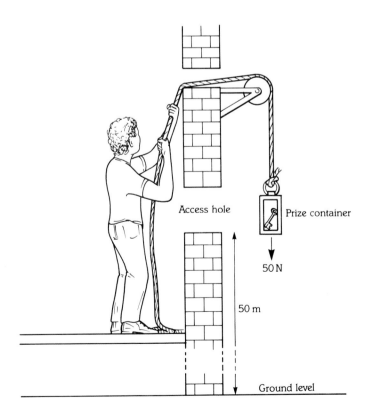

Access hole

Prize container

50 N

50 m

Ground level

Competitors have to pull on the rope to lift a cylinder. In the end of the cylinder is a chamber which holds the prize. The cylinder, which exerts a downwards force of 50 N, must be lifted 50 m (approx. 150 feet). The prize is retrieved through a small access port in the supporting wall. The contestants must do this within a limited time if they are to gain the prize.

So that the correct materials and jointing methods can be used for the triangular frame, it is important to determine the forces acting, and the direction in which they act, in the tie and strut. It is necessary to decide which components of the frame are being compressed (in compression) and which are being stretched (in tension).

The graphical representation of the equipment looks like this:

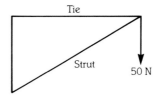

We know that the force exerted by the cylinder is 50 N acting downwards. This is represented by the force vector arrow on the left of the diagram.

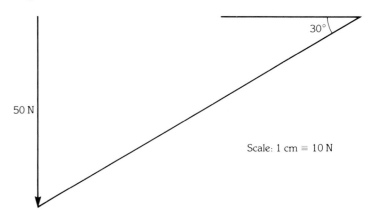

A line is drawn from the end of the arrow at the same angle as the strut. It continues up to the same level as the end of the force vector. A horizontal line is then drawn to complete the triangle of forces.

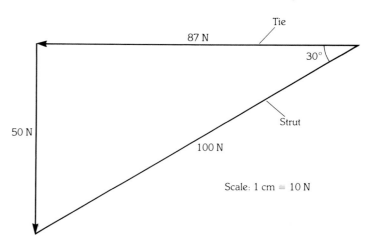

As this is a scale drawing, the length and direction of the lines for the strut and tie represent the size and direction of the forces in the two members. The strut experiences a compressive force of 99 N and the tie is subjected to a tensile force of 85 N.

For the mathematically minded, the forces can be calculated from the equations below:

$$\text{The force in the strut} = \frac{\text{Load}}{\sin 30°} = \frac{50}{0.5} = 100 \text{ N}$$

$$\text{The force in the tie} = \frac{\text{Load}}{\tan 30°} = \frac{50}{\tan 30°} = 86.6 \text{ N}$$

Ask your maths teacher for an explanation of these equations.

Evaluation

The apparatus was built and tested by a team of researchers. They had been asked to describe the strengths and weaknesses of the task.

Weaknesses
The task requires a high location.
The task is very simple and may not make interesting television.
Because of the simplicity of the task, the force required to raise the prize may need to be increased.
Anyone will win if they work hard enough! There is no test of intelligence or skill.

Strengths
The apparatus will not be particularly expensive to construct.

Conclusion
The forces to be experienced by the structure in equilibrium need to be worked out and suitable materials suggested for the final version.

The task could make acceptable television but it would be better to replace it with a more interesting assignment if there is one available.

ASSIGNMENT 7.1

Calculate the forces in the structure if the force needed to lift the prize is increased to 80 N.

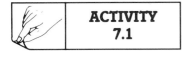
ACTIVITY 7.1

Using the information from the research section (Chapter 13), suggest a range of suitable materials that could be used to make the strut and tie.

Discuss the advantages and disadvantages of using the materials selected.

Design solution 2

Two large wooden pulleys are fixed on a supporting wall. Ropes are arranged over them, with buckets and special fittings as shown below. Special ridges on the inside of the tube and outside of the prize container will cause them to lock in position if the prize is not lifted *vertically* in the tube.

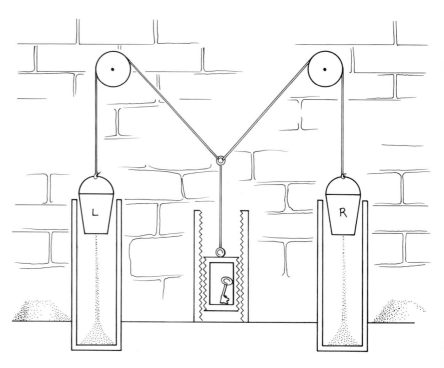

Competitors have to load sand into the containers (labelled L and R) from a pile a short distance away. As the buckets are loaded they will exert a force on the ropes. The two ropes will act together to lift the heavy prize container.

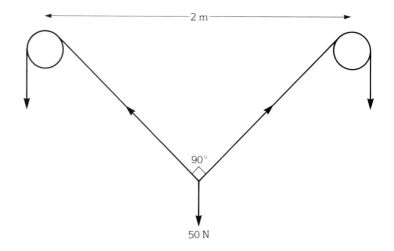

The contestants must lift the prize vertically by balancing the forces on each side. They have to do this within a limited time if they are to gain the prize. The prize container must rise at least 0.4 m.

Each bucket has a hole in the bottom and the sand that falls out of it is lost. There is a limited amount of sand available.

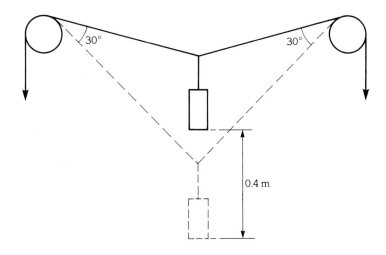

The container must rise at
least 0.4 m

If the tube becomes locked in place the competitors will need to wait
for sand to drain from the buckets (causing the prize to drop) and
then add sand to bring the lifting force back to vertical.

The prize container weighs 50 N, as in Design solution 1. At the start
the two ropes are at an angle of 90° to each other. The forces in the
ropes can be found by using the parallelogram of forces. The resultant
of these forces must be equal and opposite to the force exerted by
the prize container when it is moving steadily:

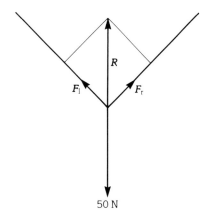

By drawing the resultant force to scale, the two components can be found:

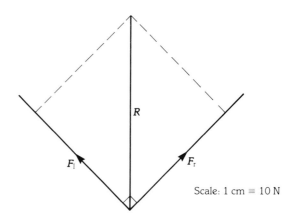

Scale: 1 cm ≡ 10 N

By measurement, $F_l = F_r = 36\,\text{N}$.

Evaluation

The game was built and tested by a team of engineers. They had been asked to describe the strengths and weaknesses of the task.

Weaknesses
A single competitor might find the task too difficult.
It would be possible to cheat by tampering with the ropes or directly lifting the container.

Strengths
The need for speed and accuracy makes the task acceptable.
If two contestants have to work together the conversation needed to produce good teamwork should be interesting to the viewers.
The risk of failure should add to the tension and amusement value.

Conclusion
The task will make good television but there are some details that will need to be sorted out before the task can be built into the programme.

ACTIVITY 7.2

Model the second design solution using a suitable kit and test it.
Calculate the forces needed to lift the prize in your solution.
Comment on your findings.

What is the maximum load that the wall will have to support in a 'winning' situation?

ASSIGNMENT 7.2

Calculate the forces in each of the ropes when the 50 N load has been lifted 0.4 m to the 30° position.

People have always sought to improve their environment. This has resulted in the use of natural structures and the construction of man-made structures that meet their needs. The development of technology has been fuelled by these needs.

Design problem

One of the most essential needs is for clean drinking water, especially in a permanently housed community.

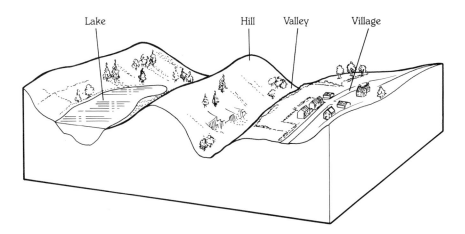

Lake   Hill   Valley   Village

Design brief

Design a solution to the problem of transporting water to the village across the valley. It should take into account modern developments in materials and structures. Conservation, social and environmental factors must also be considered.

Analysis/research

The water must flow to the village with the minimum energy input (i.e. downhill!)

The supply must flow in a water course (channel) that permits the minimum loss of water.

This channel will need to be included in any structure used to convey the water.

There are two obvious paths for the channel en route to the valley: the direct route is through the hill and the indirect route is around the hill. The valley must be crossed by a bridge (called an aqueduct) or by a 'descend, cross and rise' route.

The history of bridges and beams is very long. Natural bridges have existed since before man evolved.

Beam bridges

Trees falling across streams became simple beam bridges.

Simple beam

A simple beam consists of a straight bar or girder supported at its ends. When it is loaded the girder bends downwards, producing tension in the lower part of the beam and compression in the upper part. Beams can be short or continuous over several supports. If overloaded it will break in the middle of the span. They can have a variety of shapes, e.g. hollow box or open frame (see 'Structural sections' in Chapter 13).

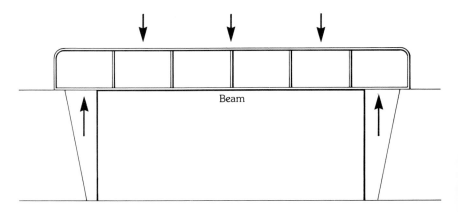

Beam

Cantilever beam

If a supporting beam is held at only one end then it is known as a **cantilever.** When it is loaded the girder bends, producing compression in the lower part of the beam and tension in the upper part. Large or wide spans are made using two cantilevers, one from each side, with any gap in the middle being bridged by a simple beam.

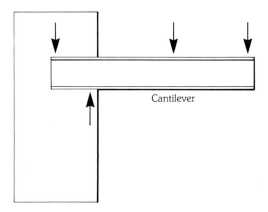

Cantilever

10 000 BC Simple beam bridges   People started to construct these as their lifestyle changed from that of hunter/gatherers to that of farmers. Wood was the best material until the 19th century when wrought iron became available. There are no examples of early wooden bridges because timber rots, but stone examples have lasted.

The medieval stone clapper bridge at Postbridge in Devon

1570 Truss girder bridge (Europe)   This was first built in timber by the Italian Andrea Palladio over the River Cismone.

1820 Truss girder bridge (N. America)   The American engineer Ithel Town patented the diagonal crossing truss. It was successful for light traffic but heavy locomotives required the truss girder to be made of interlocking triangles (a triangle cannot change its shape unless it breaks).

1847 Iron truss girder bridge   Squire Whipple produced the first iron truss and used mathematics to calculate the forces in each member.

1849 'Bow spring' girder bridge   Robert Stephenson the engineer developed this type of bridge from the work of Squire Whipple. He used this in his design for the High Level Bridge at Newcastle upon Tyne.

The High Level Bridge at Newcastle upon Tyne

1850 Box girder bridge   The Britannia Railway Bridge over the Menai Straits was another design of Robert Stephenson's. It was destroyed by fire in 1970.

The Britannia Bridge

1867 The balanced cantilever bridge   The first version of this in a modern form was built by Heinrich Gerber over the river Main at Hassfurt.

1879 The lattice girder bridge   The Tay Bridge on the East of Scotland railway route, designed by Sir Thomas Bouch, was the first bridge of this design. Due to poor calculations and inefficiency the design was faulty, and at 7 o'clock on the last Sunday in 1879 a whole train together with the upper girders of the bridge were blown away by a storm into the sea.

1948 The box bridge   The modern box girder is a rectangular-shaped tube stiffened by internal walls, making it like a series of boxes. The need for vast numbers of replacement bridges in Europe after the end of the Second World War was met by this design.

Suspension bridges

Vines dangling across rivers could grow into a simple suspension bridge.

A suspension bridge is made by spanning a gap with a cable or chain. From the cable a beam is supported. The beam is attached to the cable at many points along its length. The cable, which passes over towers, is in tension and needs strong anchorages at each end. Practically all the stresses in a suspension bridge are caused by tension.

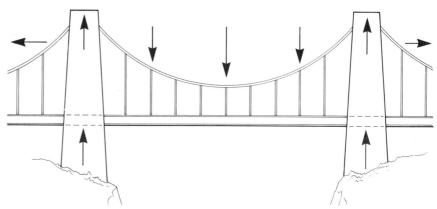

10 000 BC Simple suspension bridges No genuine Neolithic suspension bridges remain because they were made from creepers and timber.

1470 Oldest known suspension bridge This is in Yunnan Province in China. It is made from hand-forged iron chains and has a span of 69 metres.

1801 First modern suspension bridge Built by James Finlay in Pennsylvania over Jacob's creek, it was 70 ft long.

1825–60 Wire suspension bridges The best early example of this type of bridge was built over the Niagara gorge in 1855 by John Roebling.

1883 Brooklyn Bridge Started by John Roebling, but finished by his son after he died as the result of an accident at the site. It used 44 000 tons of masonry at each end of the bridge as a gravity anchorage to hold the steel cables in tension.

1940 Tacoma Narrows suspension bridge This bridge was made famous by the spectacular film recording its destruction as the result of a 42 mph wind. The wind caused the bridge to vibrate in waves then flex and twist through 90° before finally falling into Puget Sound in Washington state.

1966 Severn suspension bridge A redesigned deck was required for this bridge. It was aerodynamically tested and found to be safe. It saved 30% of the steel that would have been needed for the deck of the bridge in the original design.

Arch bridges

Boulders falling into a gorge could choke the flow of a river. Spring melt water would wash away the lower stones leaving the upper ones locked into an arch structure.

An arch is a beam that has been bent upwards. (This is best seen when viewed from the side.) The arch is prevented from spreading sideways and collapsing by strong supports on either side called **abutments.** The compression forces provided by the abutments reduce the bending effect on the beam and tension effects can be eliminated.

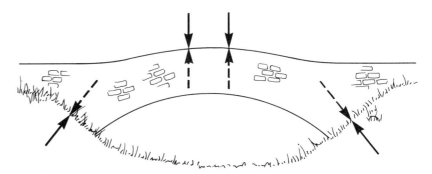

200 BC–AD 400 Roman bridges   The Romans were the first to build large bridges that were intended to last for a long time. The oldest Roman bridge is the Ponte Rotto in Rome.

The Ponte Rotto

AD 500–1500 Medieval bridges   Medieval arch bridges did not come anywhere near the standards of the Roman designs. Old London Bridge was notorious for its poor design. It took 20 years to build and had 20 spans of different sizes and shapes. It had houses on it and blocked three-quarters of the River Thames. At half tide the water was 5 ft higher on one side of the bridge than on the other.

Old London Bridge

1500–1800 Renaissance bridges A change occurred in this period. The artisan (who designed as he built) gave way to the engineer/ architect who completed a design before starting to construct it. The Rialto Bridge in Venice, completed in 1591, is a classic example of the low-rise Renaissance arch bridge.

1770–1870 Iron Bridge Abraham Darby built the first iron bridge at Coalbrookdale in 1779 over the River Severn in Shropshire.

Iron Bridge

1874 Steel bridge The first notable steel arch bridge was built by James Ead over the River Mississippi at St Louis.

1900 Reinforced concrete bridges Because concrete is strong in compression it is suitable for arch bridges. When steel reinforcement bars are added it can withstand bending in beam or cantilever form. A third section hinge is required in the middle of the bridge to allow for the contraction that occurs when the concrete sets.

1945 Pre-stressed concrete bridges This concept was thought of by Eugine Freyssinet in 1904, but the finance was not available to produce bridges designed to this idea until 1948. Freyssinet designed five bridges over the River Marne, in France, using this idea. They were completed in 1950.

A pre-stressed concrete bridge in Wales

37

Design solution

Design a solution that will solve the problem of transporting the water from one side of the valley to the other. Your solution can be set in any period of history.

Devise a specification for your historical situation. The evaluation headings below should help you.

You should explain why you think that the design you have chosen is suitable as a solution.

Evaluation

Evaluate your design in terms of the following criteria:
1) design suitability and quality
2) the materials needed to make the solution
3) the knowledge and skills needed to produce the solution.
4) Is the design suitable in environmental terms?

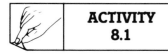
ACTIVITY 8.1

Architects use scale models to show clients what a building or structure will look like when it is finished. It is also used as a tool to work out the behaviour of wind on a structure or how surface decoration will change the appearance of a building.

A scale model of a building scheme being tested in one of the Building Research Establishment's wind tunnels

Make a model of a bridge structure. The model should work in the same way as the real bridge, i.e. a suspension bridge model should have the roadway or deck hanging from the cables slung over the towers. The cables should be fixed to secure anchorages. The deck should not be glued and fixed onto the towers with the suspension cables only there for show.

Use a large fan to generate a flow of air over the model. Design a system that will give an air supply that is free from turbulence. Then use a smoke source to reveal the pattern of air currents over the structure. Is there a condition when the wind may cause the bridge to fail? If so, why?

Structural sections

All materials are expensive! The design of a structure needs to be efficient. If too much material is used the structure will be very heavy and too costly. To make it strong enough to support its own weight it will need even more material . . . .

| **Design problem** | Investigate the efficient use of a material to withstand a compressive load. Then use the information you have gathered to assist in producing a design for a small item of furniture. |

Design brief

Design a simple paper seat that will support your weight a short distance above the ground.

Analysis/research

1) Read the section in Chapter 13 on 'Structural sections' (page 83).

2) Conduct the following investigation to find what sort of structure made from one sheet of paper will support the maximum compressive load.

The test apparatus is made up of two simple wooden shapes.

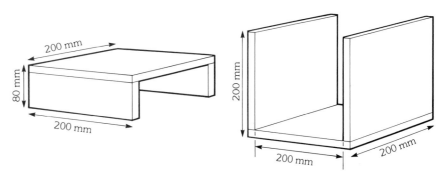

They link together with the sample structure sandwiched between them.

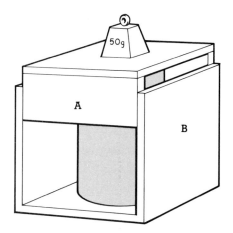

Roll or fold a sheet of paper into a shape that will support a small load. Some kind of 'honeycomb' structure is a possible approach:

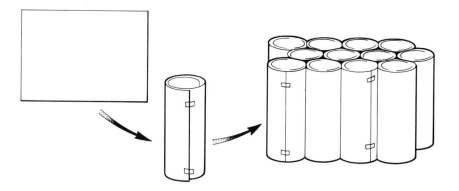

Put your structure in the test apparatus and gradually load it by adding weights until it fails. Record the maximum weight it will support before it collapses. If a variety of structures are tested the best results should be used for the design of the seat.

Evaluation

Produce a chart to summarise the result of the whole class's tests.

Which cross sections performed best under test?

What conclusions can you draw about the different shapes?

From your test data you should be able to estimate how much paper would be needed and the best structural shape for the paper to be formed into to support a person.

Design solution

Using the information gathered from your test, design a structure that will support your weight. Draw your ideas and include enough detail to enable it to be made.

Evaluation

1) You may only be able to produce a theoretical design, or possibly a small model, rather than the real thing. What factors do you think would affect the performance of the solution in practice?

2) Will your design work?

3) How easy will it be to make?

4) Does it use the available materials in the best way?

ASSIGNMENT 9.1

1) Investigate the range of possible shapes that can be used to support a compressive load.

2) Discuss what factors may influence the choice of a particular shape in practice.

Bending beams

Materials differ in their physical characteristics. It is often difficult and expensive to evaluate which is the best for a particular job.

Design problem

It is important to be able to keep the amount of material used in a design as small as possible. This will reduce costs, and by using the minimum quantities the demands on the environment will be reduced.

Design brief

Design a fair test and evaluate the performance of different shaped beams under bending loads. The beams must be made from the same material. Cantilever beams and normal beams should be compared.

Analysis/research

If you have not already done so, read the sections in Chapter 13 on:
1) 'Structural sections'
2) how to calculate bending moments and shear stresses in 'Structural calculations'.

Testing structures

Simple structures can be tested in simple ways. The more complex a structure becomes the more accurate the test must be.

Static loading
When a load is gradually applied to a structure and does not change, the load is described as a **static load.**

Dynamic loading
Changing loads constantly applied to a structure, or loads that are applied and removed suddenly, are called **dynamic loads.**

Deflection test
Beams can be tested to see whether they are stiff enough for their required purpose. A known force is applied to the beam and the amount of bend (deflection) is measured.

Does it matter where on the beam the load is placed? It may be important to consider whether the load should be a static or a dynamic load. How will the loads be applied when the structure is used in real life?

Dynamic loading

Fatigue test

This test is used to check that a part will stand a repeated cycle of loading and unloading. The cycle may be repeated many thousands of times. At the end of the test there may be no measurable change to the parts being tested, or they may have failed and broken.

Destruction test

The load on a structure is increased until the structure fails. As the structure can be tested only once it is important to gather as much information as possible during the test by any suitable methods.

Dial test indicator

This is a sensitive device for measuring deflection. The plunger is spring loaded and is connected to the pointer by a series of levers and gears. When the plunger is pressed upwards the movement is magnified by the lever and gear mechanism. The pointer travels further than the plunger and indicates the movement of the plunger against a scale on the backing plate.

Strain gauges

Strain gauges work on the principle that as a wire is stretched it becomes thinner and its electrical resistance increases. A simple electrical circuit enables a reading to be taken of the degree of strain acting on the gauge.

A simple strain gauge can be made by gluing a length of fine wire onto a piece of tissue paper. You can make and test your own strain gauge. In commercial strain gauges the wire is about 0.05 mm in diameter. Make the wire into a grid like the one shown below. Remember that the more 'folds' there are in the wire the more strain will be applied to it and the more accurate will be the reading it gives.

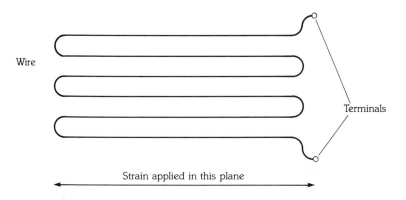

Wire

Terminals

Strain applied in this plane

The increase in electrical resistance is in proportion to the force causing the wire to stretch.

Strain gauges can only be read by converting the resistance of the wire into a measurement of voltage. When this voltage is amplified it can be used to drive a voltmeter. The voltmeter can be calibrated against known values of strain. This allows a scale to be constructed for reading the strain acting on the sample.

You will need to make two very similar gauges. Glue both gauges onto a sample of test material. The first should be glued so that strain will stretch the wire in the gauge. The second should be glued so that the strain is applied *across* the gauge and will not affect the gauge. This will eliminate the effect of a change in temperature of the gauges.

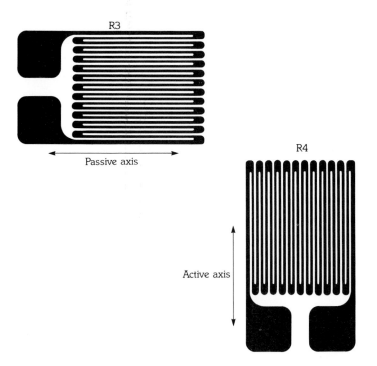

R3

Passive axis

R4

Active axis

The two strain gauges are connected into a network of resistors called a Wheatstone bridge. The test gauge is connected in the position marked R4 and the compensating gauge in the position marked R3. Most strain gauges have a resistance of between 60 Ω and 200 Ω, the most common being about 120 Ω.

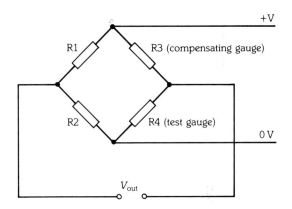

The output from the Wheatstone bridge is fed into this circuit which uses a 741 operational amplifier as a difference amplifier.

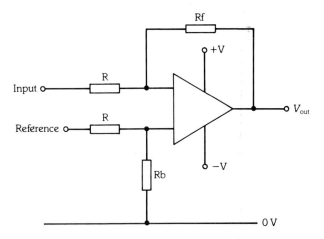

In this circuit R1 should be the same as R2 and R3 be equal to R4. Precision resistors should be used. If all four resistors have the same value, the input is the same as the output (gain of 1). V_{out} can be fed into an amplifier before being sent to a meter.

Polariscope

A polariscope can be used to study stress in some kinds of plastic and glass.

Light travels in straight lines. As it travels it vibrates in all directions about the line in which it travels.

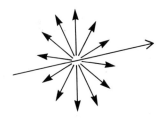

When the light goes through a polarising filter all vibrations that are not in line with the filter are removed.

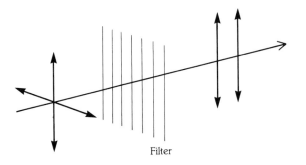

If a second filter is put after the first one and arranged so that it filters at 90 degrees to the first one *no* light passes through.

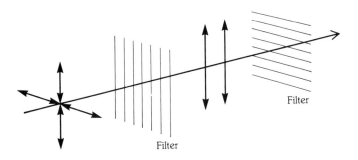

A polariscope is basically two polarising filters arranged like this.

There are certain kinds of plastics that, when stressed, polarise any light that passes through them. This effect is called **photoelasticity.** Changing the stress alters the angle of polarisation. A measure of the stress that the component is under can be found by counting the black fringes viewed on the component when it is placed between the filters in a polariscope.

Stress pattern seen when plastic is viewed through a polariscope

ACTIVITY 10.1

You can make a simple polariscope using two pairs of polarising sunglasses. Face the light and hold the lens of one pair of sunglasses in front of your eyes. Hold one lens of the second pair of glasses about six inches in front of the first one. Now slowly rotate it until the lenses appear black. The polarising filters are now at 90° to each other and no light can pass through them.

Fix the sunglasses in position so that they appear dark, using clamps, or get a friend to hold them steady. If you put something made of translucent plastic (e.g. a clear plastic ruler) between them, you should see coloured bands. How do these bands change when you bend the ruler?

ACTIVITY 10.2

Using the resources available to you in your school, select a range of differently shaped cross-sectional samples of beams. They should all be the same length and be made from the same quantity of material.

Now design a test to compare the effects of loading on each kind of beam.

Evaluation

1) Produce a chart to summarise the results of your tests.

2) Which cross sections performed best?

3) Calculate the maximum bending moment and the maximum shear stress for one sample. Compare the theoretical results with those found in practice.

Stretch

Design problem

A pupil is making an electric guitar as a major project for a GCSE examination. As part of the research for the Design Report the pupil has decided to investigate the forces produced by the strings. This information will affect the design of the guitar neck.

Design brief

Design a device that will measure the tension force in any guitar string. It should be able to test the string at its correct tuning. If possible, contrast new and used strings.

Analysis/research

The strings on a 6-string electric guitar are normally sold in sets, but individual strings can be purchased. There are different gauges of steel strings used on the electric guitar. Lighter gauge strings are thin and preferred by players who use 'bending' or 'vibrato'. This technique is common in Heavy Metal bands. Heavier gauge strings are thicker and produce a rounder, warmer sound.

The normal tuning on an electric guitar is E A D G B E. The lowest tuned strings are the nearest to the face of the player, the highest are furthest away.

The strings normally have an end that is terminated in a barrel or ball end, the other end is left as cut wire.

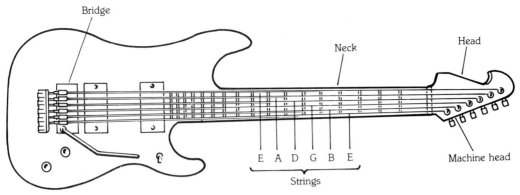

Bridge

Neck

Head

Machine head

E A D G B E

Strings

A typical set of Extra Light Gauge Strings would start with the thinnest string being 0.009 inch (0.229 mm), going up in thickness to 0.042 inch (1.067 mm). Tensioning the string of a guitar is normally done by a worm gear mechanism (called a machine head).The number of turns of the key needed to tighten the string to the correct tension would give a rough measure of the tension force, but in practice this would not be accurate enough.

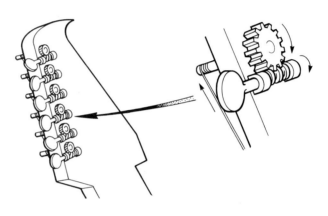

ASSIGNMENT 11.1

Find out how many cycles per second each string normally vibrates at when correctly tuned. This information can be used to help decide when the string is at the correct tension.

Design solution

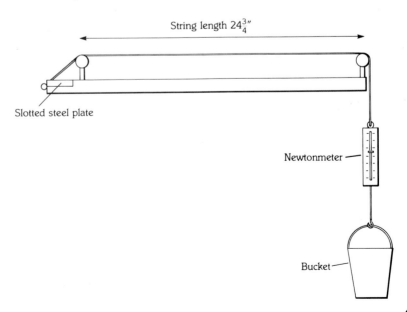

String length $24\frac{3}{4}''$

Slotted steel plate

Newtonmeter

Bucket

This design tensions the string by the use of sand loaded into a bucket. The string is linked to the newtonmeter. In turn the newtonmeter is hooked onto the handle of the bucket. If the string is passed over any sharp edges they may cause it to snap.

Sand is added to the bucket until the string vibrates at the correct frequency. You can check the frequency using a signal generator or a special guitar tuner.

The reading on the newtonmeter will give you an idea of the force applied to the string (check the accuracy of the meter). If you do not have a newtonmeter, you could weigh the bucket and sand to find the force applied to the string. Don't forget to convert kilograms to newtons!

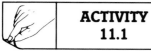

ACTIVITY 11.1

1) Construct the apparatus for testing the strings. Improve any aspect that you think may cause a poor performance by the string.

2) Test a set of new strings and calculate the total tensile force that the neck of the guitar experiences.

3) Read the section on finding component forces in Chapter 7.

ASSIGNMENT 11.2

Most guitars are assembled so that the total force exerted by the strings is applied to the neck at a slight angle.

Calculate the following:

1) the compressive force experienced by the neck
2) the force that the neck must exert to prevent it from folding forwards.

If possible, examine the truss rod mechanism that is buried in the neck of most electric guitars to counteract the bending force exerted by the strings.

Evaluation

1) Comment on your findings in the context of the structure of the musical instrument.

2) Are there any circumstances that would increase the forces acting on the guitar? If so, how are these catered for in the design of the instrument?

From theory to practice

Design problem

A local pre-school group has managed to obtain funds for the construction of play equipment. It has been decided that the biggest need is for a climbing frame. Sadly, funds are not sufficient to purchase a commercially made frame but help has been offered by a local parent who will make a frame if plans and materials can be provided.

Another source has provided plans for the climbing frame but the design is rather basic.

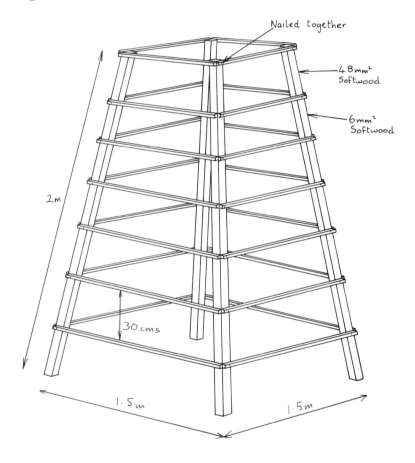

Design brief

Evaluate this design in terms of its safety for use by young children (aged 1 to 4). Suggest any improvements that might be made to the design in terms of sizes, material, construction and use.

What kind of safety factor should be used in the design of the structure?

Use calculations to prove that individual structural members are able to withstand the loads likely to be placed upon them.

Research/analysis

You should consider the following factors in your analysis of the structure:

- the age and size of the users of the climbing frame
- the size of the frame
- the structure of the frame
- the jointing methods
- the safety of the users
- the maximum static and dynamic loading of the structure
- the sizes, structural section and type of material
- the protective treatment(s) given to the material.

What action would need to be taken to free a child trapped between rungs of the frame?

Commercially made climbing frames are rigorously tested to make sure they are safe

Why structures fail

When a structure fails it often attracts public attention. Sometimes, sadly, people are killed and valuable objects lost or destroyed. Most structural failures can be analysed and the reason for the failure discovered. Some of the common reasons why a structure fails are given below.

Overloading
It is possible to see large vehicles being escorted over bridges while all other traffic is stopped. This is done to avoid the bridge's maximum designed loading being exceeded. If it is not done, damage will result, possibly causing the structure to fall.

Poor design

Structural failure will result if:

a) the *shape* of the structure is unable to withstand the loading put upon it or,

b) the *materials* that have been used in the construction are not suitable or,

c) the *joints* fail because they cannot take the load or they have been badly made due to poor technique.

Research may fail to reveal important factors that should be considered in the design. For example, there might be irregular high winds from an unusual direction or old mine workings beneath the proposed structure.

Fatigue

Wire can be broken by bending it to and fro until it breaks. This is using fatigue to our advantage. Fatigue is caused by repeated loading and unloading of a part, even though the load may be within the designed maximum for the part. The repeated loading has worn down the part's resistance to breaking and so failure occurs.

Incomplete knowledge

Even though many things are known about our world we do not know everything. Pioneers in new areas have to use all the known information, but may have to resort to guesswork when research cannot reveal any more information. Their decision may affect your life!

Safety factors

To try to allow for unforeseen circumstances, designers aim to design structures that will withstand 150% or 200% of the expected maximum load. This allows a 50% or 100% **safety factor** to be designed into the structure. (Read the sections on 'Stress, strain and elasticity' and 'Safety factors' in Chaper 13.)

An alternative method of adding a safety factor to a design is to include an additional part that is not normally necessary. For example, on the vertical tailplane of all aircraft is a hinged control surface that helps the plane to turn left or right. The hinge is a vital part of the design. If it fails, the control surface will be ripped away because of the speed of the plane and it will crash. Aircraft are checked very frequently, but a small crack may be missed, especially if it is on the inside of the hinge surface. The addition of an extra set of hinge pieces will mean that if one set fails in flight the plane will be controllable and land safely.

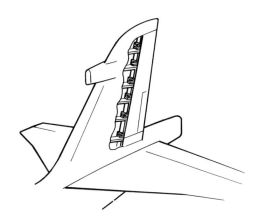

Hinged control surface on an aircraft fin

Many cars have dual braking systems, two complete systems that normally work together. In the event of damage to one system the other system will be efficient enough to enable the driver to stop the car safely.

ACTIVITY 12.1

Having evaluated the design, produce a new and improved design for the structure that is both safer and stronger.

ASSIGNMENT 12.1

Read the section on 'Structural calculations' in Chapter 13. Given that the maximum force exerted by the user(s) on one rung of the frame is a weight of $4\frac{1}{2}$ stone, approximately 28 kg or 280 N, calculate for the original climbing frame design:

1) the maximum bending moment experienced by the lowest rung in the frame (this rung has an effective length of 1.3 m);
2) the reactions and shear forces experienced by the lowest rung in the frame. Draw the shear force diagram for that rung.

Repeat the calculations for your own design. *Is* your design stronger and safer than the original?

Bow's notation

Bow's notation is a method of labelling forces.

In this space diagram there are three forces acting on a point.

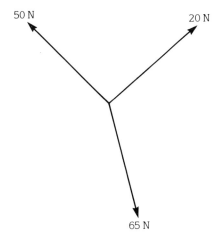

The space between each of the forces is labelled with a capital letter. Start with the letter **A** then label each space between the forces, working round clockwise.

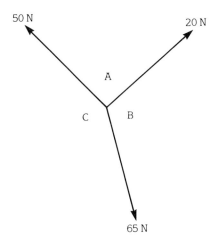

Each force can be clearly identified by the letters in the spaces either side of it. The 50 N force is CA, the 20 N force AB and the 65 N force BC.

With a complicated structure the reason for using Bow's notation becomes obvious. When trying to clearly identify the parts of the structure, start by finding out where the forces are acting on the structure. Mark them on the drawing.

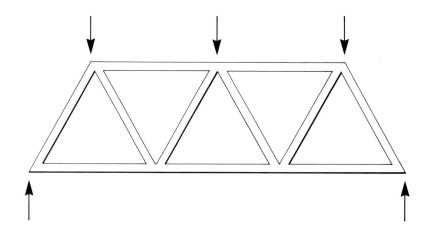

Label the spaces between the forces and the structural members. Start at the top left side of the drawing and then work in a clockwise direction, spiralling inwards towards the centre of the structure.

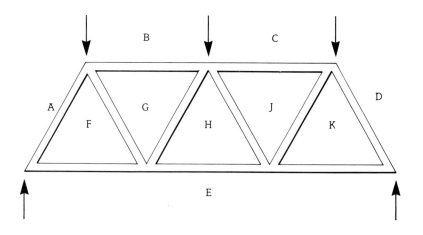

It is now possible to identify FG and JH without confusion, even though they are very similar.

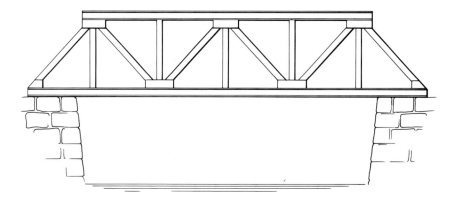

A Warren girder bridge has this type of structure

Jointing techniques

Common basic techniques

	Timber	Metal	Plastic	Textiles	Ceramics	Concrete	Paper
Adhesives	✓	✓	✓	✓	✓		✓
Mechanical fastenings	✓	✓	✓	✓		✓	✓
Screws	✓	✓	✓				
Nut & bolt	✓	✓	✓			✓	✓
Cotters	✓	✓					
Clips		✓	✓	✓			✓
Interlocking	✓	✓	✓	✓		✓	✓
Rivets		✓	✓	✓			✓
Soldering		✓					
Brazing		✓					
Welding		✓	✓				

Adhesives

Selecting the correct type of adhesive is important if a strong joint is to be made. The decision depends on the materials to be joined, the required strength of the join and the environmental conditions.

Jointing materials with adhesives alone has many advantages:

It can be quicker than mechanical jointing.
Mechanical jointing can be heavier than glueing.
The parts are not weakened by drilling or cutting.
The stresses are spread evenly across the joint.
The joint requires little skill to produce.

Using an adhesive to join an aluminium seal to a car bonnet

The disadvantages of using adhesives are:

The joint is weak when shear forces are applied to it.
The joints can be badly affected by temperature.
It can be more expensive than mechanical jointing.
Adhesives must be allowed time to set or cure

To make a strong joint, the glued area should be as large as possible and the gap between the surfaces must be very small.

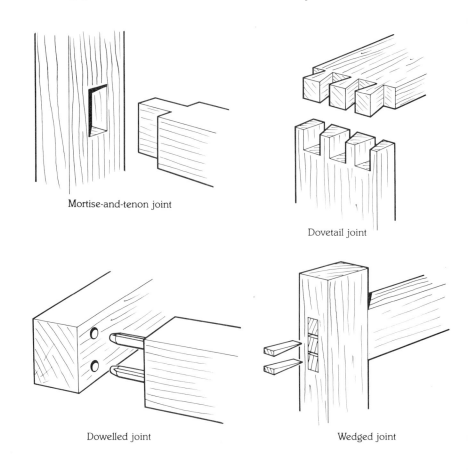

Mortise-and-tenon joint

Dovetail joint

Dowelled joint

Wedged joint

Mechanical joints and fastenings

These are normally semi-permanent methods of holding parts together. Screws and nuts and bolts all rely on a screw thread to produce a clamping action.

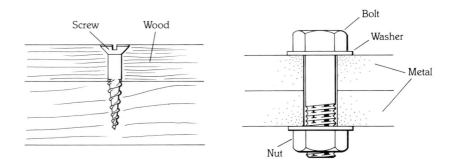

Riveting materials together is a relatively quick process that requires a minimum of tools and a small degree of skill. Traditional riveted joints have been replaced to a degree by the use of pop rivets. These are quick to install and are widely used.

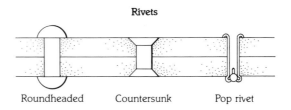

The advantages of using mechanical fastenings are:

They can be completed quickly.
Mechanical jointing is strong.
Moderate temperatures rarely affect the joint.

The disadvantage of using mechanical fastenings are:

They often add weight to the structure.
Mechanical jointing can concentrate stresses and produce weak points.
Production costs can be increased by the use of jointing.
They can require specialist skill.

Soldering and brazing

The two most common types of solder are 'soft solder' (a lead–tin alloy) and 'hard' or silver solder.

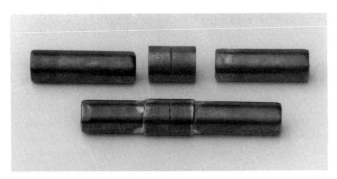

A soldered connection on a straight section of copper pipe

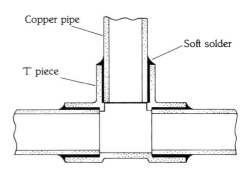

Cross-section of a soldered joint

The advantages of soldering are:

There is no other way of permanently joining electrical components in a circuit.
Soldering adds little weight to the joint.
Soldering can be as quick as mechanical jointing.
The strength of a soldered joint is high.
Stresses are rarely concentrated in soldered joints.
Soldered joints are not affected by normal household temperatures.

The disadvantages of soldering are:

Reliable jointing requires good preparation.
A reliable energy source is needed to heat the joint – gas or electricity.
Soldering requires some skill to produce reliable joints.
Some solders require expensive metals and are costly.

Brazing uses a melted alloy called brass to make the joint. It requires a higher temperature but gives a relatively stronger joint. The advantages and disadvantages are similar to soldering.

Welding

Welding occurs when two pieces of a material are joined by localised melting. This is most commonly used with metals but the same technique can be used with thermoplastics. Heat is applied to the plastic surfaces to be joined, to melt them. The pieces are held together so that their surfaces bond together as the plastic solidifies again.

The advantages of welding are:

Welding adds little weight to the joint.
Welding can be as quick as mechanical jointing.
The strength of a welded joint is high.
Welded joints are not affected by temperature.

The disadvantages of welding are:

Reliable jointing requires good preparation.
Some skill is needed to produce reliable joints.
A reliable source of energy is required. Welding plants using gas or electricity are heavy.

Materials

Timber

A typical softwood tree

A typical hardwood tree

Tree cells fall into two structural patterns. The types of tree that have long thin leaves and stay green all the year around are called **softwoods.** The cells of this type of tree are relatively long and thin.

The types of tree that have broad leaves and often shed them at the onset of winter are called **hardwoods.** In tropical areas the shedding of leaves will occur throughout the year. The cells of these trees are relatively broad and short.

Nature produces many varieties of tree each with its own characteristic wood structure. At first glance a piece of wood may appear to be one type, but on closer inspection it can often turn out to be a different species of wood. Don't rely on first impressions when identifying a piece of timber.

When the wood from trees is cut ready for use it is cut so that the cells run along the length of the timber. The plank of wood has been cut 'with the grain'. This means that this piece of wood will be strong in tension and compression along its length, but it will be weakest when forces act across the grain.

Tree species have different cell structures. This difference in structure affects the properties of the wood obtained from that type of tree. Some timbers are stronger than others. Some are lighter or heavier than others for a set size. Typical densities for a selection of hardwoods and softwoods are shown in this table.

Densities of some timbers

Softwoods

Scots pine	26 lb per cubic foot
Douglas fir	32–34 lb per cubic foot
Yew	42 lb per cubic foot

Hardwoods

Balsa	6 lb per cubic foot
African mahogany	30–38 lb per cubic foot
Beech	45 lb per cubic foot
Ebony	77 lb per cubic foot

The weight of a timber will add to the static load applied to a structure.

Natural wood cannot always be found with the required properties for a design. Natural timbers can have defects like knot holes, warping or damage caused when the tree was felled. The maximum available width of a board is almost the width of a living tree. This may take many years to grow and there is only one board of this maximum size that can be cut from each grown tree. Wider sizes require several pieces of wood to be joined together.

Because of economic pressures and the demand for timber, man-made boards have been developed. There are several kinds of man-made board; some of the most common are hardboard, plywood, blockboard and chipboard.

Hardboard
This is a thin board, normally 3 mm thick, made from compressed timber waste. It is often used to cover the surface of a structure cheaply. It is not very strong in tension or compression.

Plywood
This is a manufactured board made from layers of timber glued together. The grain of each piece is laid at 90° to the next layer. It is very strong, but also heavy because of the amount of glue needed to join the layers together. It is also used because of its good strength-to-weight ratio. Light aircraft wings can be designed to be covered with thin plywood.

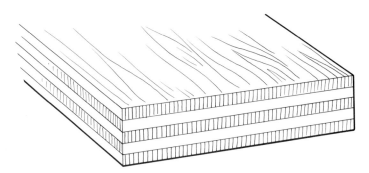

Blockboard
This material is made from blocks of timber glued together to form a thick, flat board and then covered with a thin veneer of timber. It is a cheap type of medium strength board.

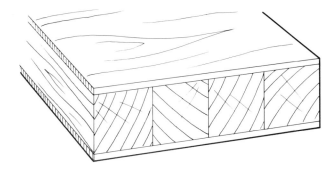

Chipboard
This board is made out of wood chips compressed and glued together. The board is not very strong in any direction and breaks easily because there are no long fibres in the wood that can resist

breaking. It is very cheap and can be made in wide boards. It is very heavy because of the amount of glue needed to hold the wood chips together. The chips are compressed together, making the board denser than normal timber.

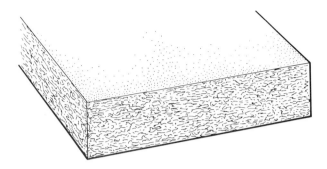

Chipboard on its own does not look very good, the surface is full of small holes which make painting difficult. Gluing thin wood veneers or plastic laminate on the surfaces is the best way of making the chipboard look better (see the next section). It is used where medium-low strength is acceptable. Chipboard is available in wide boards, 2400 mm × 1220 mm is a standard size.

Veneered chipboard

When a veneer is glued onto a sheet of chipboard the appearance of the board is dramatically improved. The board can pass for natural timber to the inexperienced eye. It has very similar characteristics to ordinary chipboard. The veneer applied to the surface is not restricted to wood: melamine and formica are often glued to the board to give a waterproof and heat-resistant surface. D.I.Y. kitchen units are almost exclusively made from this material.

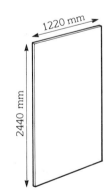

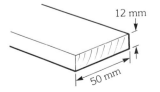

Timbers are normally purchased in the following standard forms.

Man-made boards: in sheets, normally 2440 mm × 1220 mm or 150 mm².
Natural timbers: either by length at a standard cross section, e.g. 1 m × 50 mm × 12 mm;

or by area at a standard thickness, e.g. 2 m² × 12 mm (this would be delivered in the form of several boards of various lengths 12 mm thick; the total area would be equal to 2 m²)
or by cubic foot (this would be delivered in the form of several boards of various lengths and thicknesses as specified in your order.

Metals

The structure and properties of all materials are based on the arrangement of the component atoms. The atoms in metals are linked together in regular patterns that form crystals. Metals can be described as **crystalline solids.**

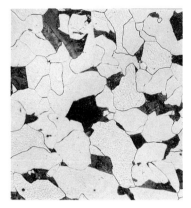

Crystals of iron
(magnified ×100)

The crystalline structure of a metal is formed by the way in which the atoms arrange themselves as the molten metal cools. When a piece of metal is carefully examined under a microscope the crystals can be seen.

These crystals are formed as the metal cools, and disappear when the metal is heated again to a critical temperature. They grow again to form a new pattern each time the metal is cooled. The rate of cooling is a critical factor affecting the size and shape of the crystals.

The size and shape of the crystals can vary considerably. Two similar pieces of metal can have a very different arrangement of crystals and will behave differently in use. One piece may stand a large force, the other may crack and break. The design of the corners in a casting is an example of this. The crystals grow inwards from the edge as the metal cools, forming long crystals.

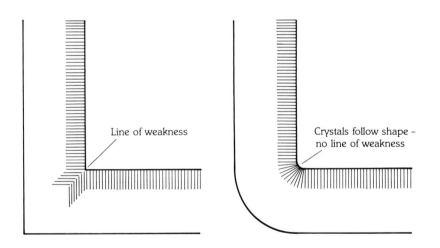

The angle in the corner of the casting has caused the crystal grains to form a plane of weakness. This can be removed by re-designing the piece with a curved corner. This causes a different pattern of grain growth and no weak zone.

Metals can be made up of a single chemical element, or more than one element. When metals are made up from more than one element they are called **alloys**. For example, aluminium is a pure metal, but steel is made from a mixture of iron and carbon, and is an alloy.

Metals are divided into two main categories:
ferrous (metals or alloys containing iron) and
non ferrous (metals or alloys not containing iron).

Metals are normally purchased in the following standard forms:
Bar: flat, round, hexagonal or rectangular
Tube: round or rectangular
Sheet: thickness measured in mm or SWG (Standard Wire Gauge)
Structural section: e.g. 'I' or angle.

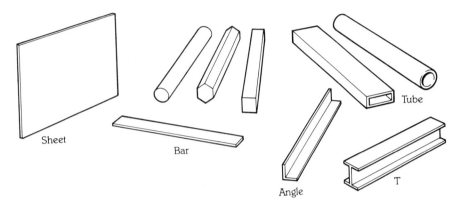

Ceramics

There are several different ceramic substances. One of the most common is fired clay.

Clay is formed by the geological weathering of an igneous rock. Clays are types of chemical compound called aluminosilicates – alumina and silica, chemically combined with water. But no clay is pure and they always contain many other materials, often in very small quantities.

When viewed under the microscope, the clay particles are flat and hexagonal. The particles stick to each other, but will slide if there is water present, allowing the clay to be easily manipulated and shaped.

There are several basic types of clay mixture, which are fired at different temperatures. When the clay is fired, a complex, irreversible process starts.

At 200 °F/93 °C the atmospheric moisture is driven off.
At 600 °F/316 °C all the chemically combined water is driven off.
Earthernware clays mature at 1800 °F/902 °C.
Ball clays (finer than earthenware clays) mature at 2300 °F/1260 °C.
Fire clays (which resist heat) mature at 2700 °F/1402 °C.

When the clay is fired it becomes **vitrified.** This means that certain components of the clay melt and combine together to form a crystalline structure within the clay. This crystalline structure causes the clay to become hard and durable. Fired clay is stronger in compression than it is in tension.

Ceramic materials are not made only out of fired clay. Ceramic crystals which have extremely high strength can be grown from any chemical that forms needle-like crystals, e.g. silicon, sapphire (aluminium oxide), zinc oxide and diamond. They are made by allowing a saturated solution to evaporate. As the solution evaporates many fine, single crystal needles form. The length of the crystals is very small and they are so fine that they are hardly visible even when using an optical microscope.

The strength and ability to withstand deformation of crystalline structures has not yet been fully evaluated. This is the main area of development of composite materials. Fibreglass, Kevlar and carbon fibre represent the current high-tech answer to the requirement for high strength materials.

Clays are normally purchased in bags of a set weight, e.g. 10 kg.

Bricks and stone

Bricks, like ceramics, are made from fired clay. They come in a wide variety of types, depending on the kind of clay used, the method of firing and the subsequent treatment.

The most durable structural material is natural stone.
There are many types of stone. It is a naturally occurring resource and was created in the earth's crust as our plant was formed. Stone is strong in compression but weak in tension.

Bricks are sold in standard multiples of 1000 or individually for decorative bricks. Stone is sold by weight.

Concrete

Concrete is a mixture of four basic materials: cement, sand and stones (aggregate) and water.

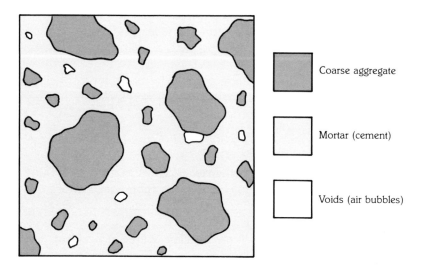

Coarse aggregate

Mortar (cement)

Voids (air bubbles)

Cement is the active ingredient in the mix. It is made from a crushed and heated mixture of limestone or chalk and clay. When thoroughly mixed with water, a chemical reaction takes place. Concrete forms as a complex crystalline structure that bonds to the aggregate, linking the mixture together. When the concrete has finished reacting and the water has dried out, the concrete has completely set.

Concrete is strong in compression

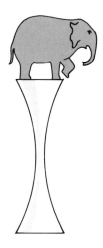

and weak in tension.

Why do I get these jobs?

In a horizontal beam under load there are tension *and* compression forces.

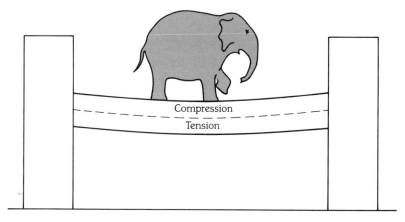

Compression

Tension

When concrete is cast into beams, steel reinforcement is put in to support the finished beam. The strengthening reinforcement is placed only where the concrete beam is in tension and weak.

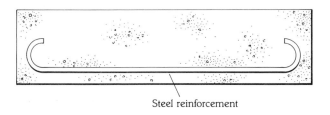

Steel reinforcement

Cement, sand and aggregate are sold by weight, usually 25 kg or 50 kg bags. Ready mixed concrete is sold in cubic metres.

Plastics

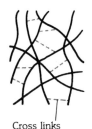

Cross links softened by heat

Cross-links partially softened by heating

Permanent cross-links

Plastics have a structure based on the atoms being linked together in molecular chains. When the plastic is set, bonding links form between the chains, locking them together. There are three main kinds of plastics.

Thermoplastics
This type have bonds between the molecular chains that dissolve each time the thermoplastic is heated. Thermoplastics can be re-shaped many times. Common types of plastics in this category are Nylon, polystyrene and acrylic (Perspex).

Elastomers
This type of plastics have molecular chains that have a small number of cross-linking bonds that are permanent. This allows the molecule chains to move when the elastomer is heated. Because of the permanent bonds, there is a limit to the amount of change that can be imposed upon the plastic before the material is damaged. Rubber is an example of an elastomer.

Thermosetting plastics
These plastics have bonds between the molecule chains that are permanent. They form when the plastic is first moulded into shape and will not disappear when heated. This type of plastic can be shaped only once. Thermosetting plastics are often used as joining agents, as they can behave like a glue. For example, polyester resin is used to bond glassfibre matting to form glass-reinforced plastic (GRP). This type of plastic is very good at resisting the effects of heat, keeping its shape at high temperatures.

Plastics are normally purchased in the following standard forms:
Bar: flat, round, hexagonal and rectangular
Tube: round and rectangular
Sheet: thickness measured in mm or SWG
Liquid: (for resins)
Powder: for dip coating
Granules: for injection moulding

Newton's Laws

Newton's First Law
A body will remain at rest or continue to move with uniform motion in a straight line unless acted upon by an external force.

Newton also observed that in real life, for objects to remain still when a force is acting on them, there must be an equal and opposite force acting on the object that is stopping it from moving. He produced a law covering this situation.

Newton's Third Law
To every action there is an equal and opposite reaction.

Safety factors

Provided that the loading of a material does not exceed its elastic limit (see page 73), it will return to its original length when the force is removed.

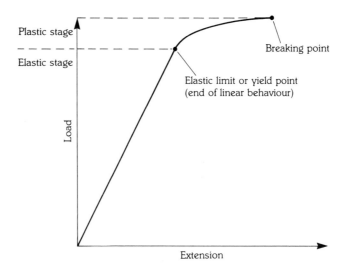

Structures are normally designed with a safety factor. A safety factor of 2 means that the design is stressed to half the load that will cause failure (yield point). A factor of 3 means that the loading is one-third of the failure load. The more consistent the quality of the material (metals and plastics) the lower the safety factor. Natural materials (timbers) are usually given a higher safety factor.

However, repeated loading and unloading may cause the material to fail. The sample will suffer **fatigue.** Predicting when any material will fail is difficult. Experiments can be carried out with different loads being applied and removed many times to determine just when a particular sample will fail. As you would expect, lighter loads will not cause failure as early as heavier loads.

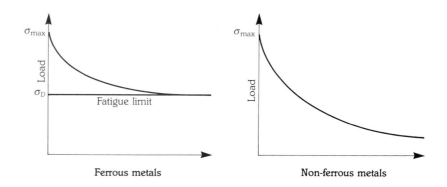

Ferrous metals   Non-ferrous metals

In the graphs, σ_{max} is the smallest load that will cause the metal sample to break at once. As the load is reduced, more cycles of applying and removing it are needed to make the sample fail. With ferrous metals, if the load is small enough failure through fatigue will never occur. Any number of repeated cycles can be experienced when the load is less than σ_D, the **fatigue limit.**

By using this information a design engineer can ensure that the loading on a particular part does not exceed the fatigue limit.

Non-ferrous metals do not have a fatigue limit and will eventually fail however small the load.

Strengthening techniques for materials

Structures made of solid materials are heavy and expensive to produce. It is important to use the minimum amount of material in a structure to keep the costs as low as possible. The more material is used the heavier the structure becomes and the more material is needed to support it!

One method of reducing the amount of material and cost is to make the structure from hollow materials. Hollow tubes have the same resistance to bending as solid tubes but are much lighter and cheaper because they use less material.

Scaffolding poles need to be strong but relatively light

Reducing the thickness of sheet material to save weight will make it prone to bending and distortion. The thinner the material the easier it will be for it to bend in the wrong directions.

Sheet steel is used in the construction of car bodies. To strengthen it without adding more material it is bent or deformed. The **forming** makes the steel become a three-dimensional shape, but it requires energy to bend it. **Corrugation** makes sheet material rigid across the corrugations, but flexible parallel with them.

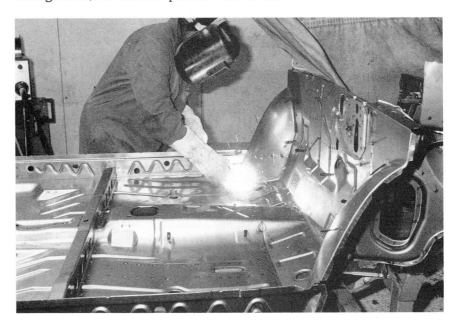

Sheet steel is formed or bent into car body panels, giving the steel added strength

Lamination as a strengthening process is best seen in plywood (see page 62). Layers of timber are glued with the grain of each layer running at 90° to the previous layer. This produces an attractive and strong timber-based material that has better strength characteristics than a single similar-sized piece of wood.

Laminated beam

Laminated beams are often used to support the roof in modern buildings

Careful design can save expensive materials without sacrificing strength.

Special strengthening techniques can be used for metals.

Alloying

By mixing different metals together new substances with different physical properties can be produced. A metallic material made from two or more chemically pure metals is called an **alloy**.

Alloys are produced to give characteristics that pure metals do not possess. For example, copper and aluminium are weak metals in tension, but a mixture of 5% copper and 95% aluminium produces an aluminium alloy twice as strong as copper.

Pure iron is very hard and brittle, but the addition of carbon to the iron produces steel, which is much tougher and less likely to break. The addition of chromium to the alloy produces stainless steel which resists corrosion (rusting).

Age hardening

An aluminium alloy called 'Duralumin' made from 3.5% copper, 0.5% magnesium and 96% aluminium, shows a characteristic called **age hardening.** The metal slowly increases in hardness after annealing (a softening process). After about four or five days the strength of the metal has dramatically increased. There is little further increase in strength after this time.

Stress, strain and elasticity

If you are designing a structure you should be aware of what will happen to the materials in that structure. You need to know what happens to materials when they are loaded.

Elasticity

If you pull on a rubber band gently, it will stretch. When you release the tension it will return to its original length. This stretching and contraction is called elastic behaviour.

When you plot a graph of the increase in length (extension) against the force producing the stretch it should look like this:

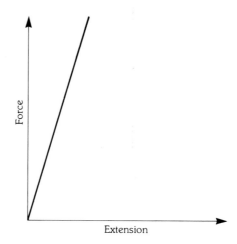

A small force causes a small extension, a larger force will cause the rubber band to extend to a proportionally greater length.

This property was investigated by a scientist named Robert Hooke (1653-1703). He studied the information and then found an expression that explained what happens when a material is loaded with a tensile force.

Hooke's law
The change in the length of a piece of material caused by an applied force is proportional to the size of the applied force.

Different materials behave in different ways under tension. For example, in an experiment two different material samples have been loaded and stretched. The results of the experiment are shown on the graph below.

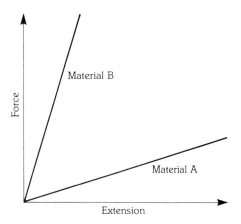

Material A stretches more than Material B for a given tensile load.

If the material is loaded too much its behaviour can be unpredictable, as shown below in the load-extension graph for mild steel.

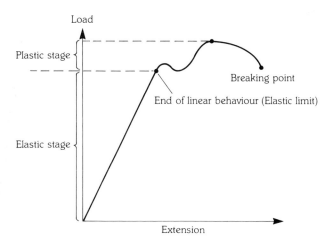

When the limit of elastic behaviour is exceeded the material behaves plastically and will not return to its original size again. It will remain permanently stretched when the load is removed.

It is important to use any stressed material so that its load and extension are on the straight part of the graph.

Stress

The illustration below shows two rectangular bar columns.

Bar A has a cross-sectional area of 20 mm².
Bar B has a cross-sectional area of 7 mm².

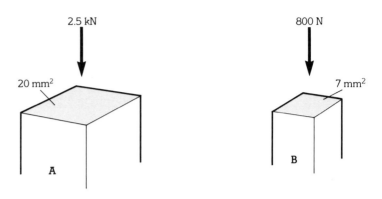

Bar A is carrying a load of 2.5 kN.
Bar B has a load of 800 N.

It is difficult to see which bar would be the more likely to break under load.

The best way of evaluating the situation is to calculate the load (stress) on a unit of area, usually 1 mm².

$$\text{Stress} = \frac{\text{Load or Force}}{\text{Area}}$$

The Greek letter (σ) sigma is used as a symbol for stress, so the equation is written as

$$\text{Stress} \; (\sigma) = \frac{F}{A}$$

For bar A this would be $\dfrac{2500\,\text{N}}{20\,\text{mm}^2} = 125\,\text{N/mm}^2$

For bar B this would be $\dfrac{800\,\text{N}}{7\,\text{mm}^2} = 114.28\,\text{N/mm}^2$

Stress is a force measured in N/mm².

Necking

When a material is stressed too much it stretches and becomes thinner. This is called **necking**.

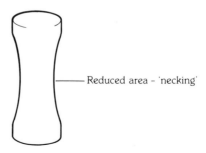

Reduced area – 'necking'

These thin areas of material have an increased stress loading because the cross-sectional area is reduced. This will lead to premature failure of the material.

Strain

When materials are put under tension or compression they respond to the load, stretching or squashing according to the type of load. This response is called **strain.**

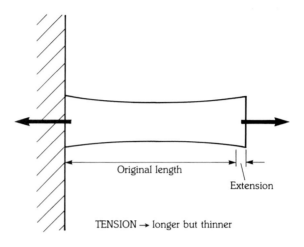

TENSION → longer but thinner

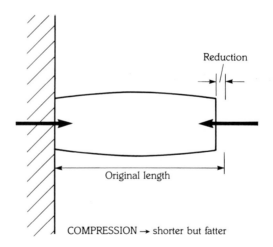

COMPRESSION → shorter but fatter

Remember, when a material is loaded in one direction changes occur in other dimensions. In tension a bar becomes thinner and longer, in compression the same bar becomes thicker and shorter. This can be expressed as:

$$\text{Strain} = \frac{\text{Change in length}}{\text{Original length}} = \frac{\Delta L}{L}$$

Young's modulus

This is a ratio of the stress and the strain acting on material. It enables engineers to compare the behaviour of materials under load.

A variety of materials under test produce results like this:

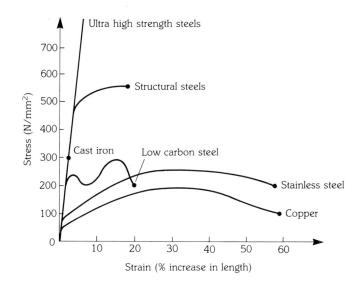

Young's modulus is represented in engineering terms by the letter epsilon (ε). It is measured in kN/mm^2.

Stiff materials such as high strength steels have a high modulus. Elastic materials such as copper have a low modulus (number).

$$\text{Young's modulus, } \varepsilon = \frac{\text{Stress}}{\text{Strain}}$$

Structural calculations

Turning moments

A beam is a length of material used to support a load.

Cantilever beam

This diagram needs to be simplified so that we can work out what forces are acting on the beam and the force that needs to be exerted by the wall to stop the beam falling.

The beam is 3 m long and 0.3 m of the beam is in the wall. The gymnast exerts a force of 50 newtons on the beam at a distance of 2.5 m from the wall. The information is drawn like this:

The point where the beam enters the wall is shown as an arrow head and is the fulcrum point.

To calculate the clockwise turning moment acting on the bar we use this equation.

$$\text{Turning moment} = \text{Force} \times \text{Distance}$$

or

$$M = F \times d$$

The answer will be in newton metres (Nm).

Note: All the measurements must be converted to metres before starting to work out the solution.

Substituting the figures into the equation:

$$M = F \times d$$
$$= 50 \times 2.5$$
$$= 125\,\text{Nm}$$

The gymnast exerts a turning moment on the beam of 125 Nm.

To find the force that balances the beam and holds it steady, we must again assume that the beam is in equilibrium and that the beam's weight is ignored. What force is needed at the left end of the beam to balance the force on the right end?

The turning force on the right side of the beam must balance the turning force on the left end for the beam to balance. The equation for the turning force on the right end of the beam is:

$$M_R = F_1 \times d_1$$

The same equation applies to the left end.

$$M_L = F_2 \times d_2$$

For the beam to balance, the solution to the two equations must be the same. When the equation is rearranged to give the balancing moments it looks like this (note the balancing moments cancel out and disappear):

$$F_2 \times d_2 = F_1 \times d_1$$

Rearranging the equation in terms of F_2,

$$F_2 = \frac{F_1 \times d_1}{d_2}$$

Inserting the figures into the equation,

$$F_2 = \frac{50 \times 2.5}{0.3}$$

$$= \frac{125}{0.3}$$

$$F_2 = 416.67 \, \text{N}$$

A force of 416.67 newtons acting 0.3 m from the pivot point (fulcrum) will balance the beam and maintain equilibrium.

QUESTION: What do you do if there is more than one force acting on a beam?
ANSWER: Add the turning moments together.

When several forces are acting on a beam the turning moment for each beam is calculated individually. Then they are all added together and the total turning moment on that side calculated.

Girl 1 exerts a force of 50 N, girl 2 exerts a force of 53 N. This can be shown simply as:

The equation for this calculation is:

$$\text{Total turning moment} = (F_1 \times d_1) + (F_2 \times d_2)$$

The (Force × Distance) moment calculations are worked out first and then added together. If there are more than two moments acting on one side of the beam then they are just added together in the equation.

Substituting the figures,

$$\text{Total turning moment} = (50 \times 2.5) + (53 \times 3)\,\text{Nm}$$
$$= 125 + 159\,\text{Nm}$$
$$= 284\,\text{Nm}$$

Beam reactions

A beam is normally supported at both ends, as when used as a bridge. The weight of the beam plus any load on it press down at the ends where the beam is supported.

For the beam to stay in place the supports must be able to support any load with an equal and opposite force.

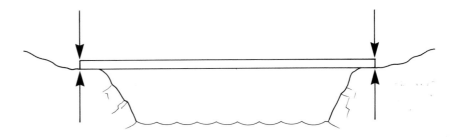

If the beam is not carrying any load then the weight of the beam is divided equally between the left and right ends.

How can you work out the load in the left and right ends of the beam and thus the reactions in the supports at both ends? This beam is subjected to two forces:

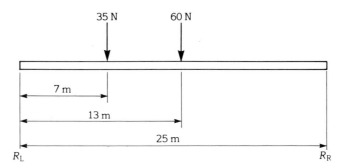

There is a force of 35 N acting at 7 m from the left end and a force of 60 N acting 13 m from the left end. The whole beam is 25 m long.

The calculation to find the left and right reactions is in three easy parts.

1) Find all the turning moments acting on the left end.
   Add the moments together.

$$\text{Turning moment} = \text{Force} \times \text{Distance}$$

$$
\begin{aligned}
35 \times 7 &= 245 \\
60 \times 13 &= \underline{780} \\
&\quad 1025\,\text{Nm total}
\end{aligned}
$$

2) Divide the total turning moment by the length of the beam.
   (This will calculate the force acting downwards at the right end of the beam).

$$\frac{1025\,\text{Nm}}{25\,\text{m}} = 41\,\text{N}$$

The force exerted by the right end of the beam = 41 N.

3) Find the force acting in the left end of the beam.
   Subtract the force acting in the right end from the total force acting on the beam.

Total force acting on the beam = 60 N + 35 N = 95 N

Force acting on the left end of the beam = 95 N − 41 N = 54 N

So R_R must be 41 N and R_L is 54 N.

Shear force diagrams

When considering shear forces (SF) we have to decide whether the shear force is positive or negative. If the right side of the beam is displaced downwards or the left upwards we say the shear force is **positive.** The shear force is **negative** if the beam is displaced the opposite way.

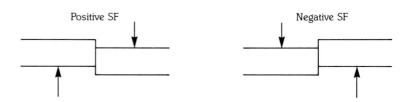

Let us calculate the shear force at all points in the beam shown below. Note that the answer is in the form of a diagram.

1) Calculate the beam reactions at A (R_A) and B (R_B).
   Take the moments about A:

$$R_B = \frac{50 \times 2}{8} = 12.5\,\text{kN}$$

$$R_A + R_B = 50\,\text{kN}$$

therefore $\quad R_A = 50\,\text{kN} - R_B = 50 - 12.5 = 37.5\,\text{kN}$

The reaction at A acts upwards (positive). There are no other forces between A and C so the shear force must be constant (37.5 kN) until C. It drops to 12.5 kN and is then constant until B. Because the overall forces are in equilibrium the forces start and finish on the same line, 0, on the diagram.

The forces in a cantilever beam can be calculated by drawing the shear force diagram.

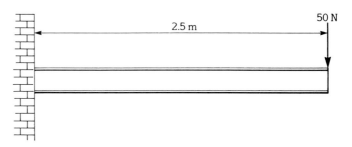

Because the beam is in equilibrium the reaction at the wall will be 50 N.

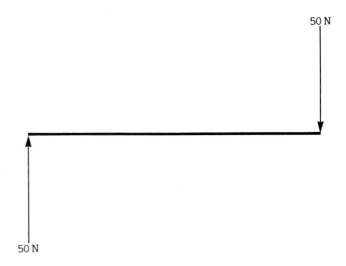

The shear force must be 50 N and constant all the way along the cantilever to the point where the force is applied.

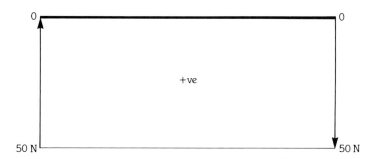

By careful scale drawing the shear force can be calculated at any point along the beam. Here it is 50 N at all points.

Bending moments

The amount that a beam bends depends upon the length of the beam and the force applied to it. The standard convention for describing a bending moment is this.

If a beam is sagging the bending moment is *positive*.
If a beam is hogging the bending moment is *negative*.

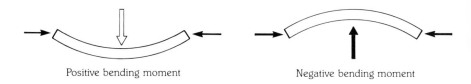

Positive bending moment   Negative bending moment

Using the beam example given on page 80.

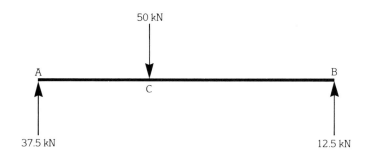

the bending moment at C can be calculated from this equation:

$$\text{Bending moment} = \frac{W \times d_1}{d_{total}}(d_{total} - d_1)$$

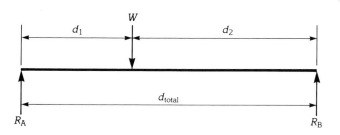

Substituting in the figures,

$$\text{Bending moment at C} = \frac{50\,\text{kN} \times 2\,\text{m}}{8\,\text{m}}(8\,\text{m} - 2\,\text{m})$$

$$= \frac{100\,000}{8}(6) = 75\,000\,\text{Nm}$$

The bending moment rises steadily and uniformly from A to C. This is drawn as:

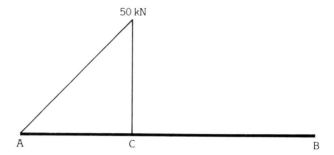

The bending moment also increases uniformly from B to C.

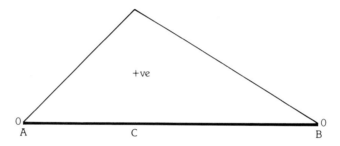

The bending moment is positive along the length of the beam. It is greatest at the point where the load is applied and zero where the beam is supported.

For this cantilever beam, the bending moment is negative.

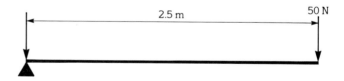

The bending moment for a cantilever beam is least where the force is applied and greatest where the beam is supported by the wall.

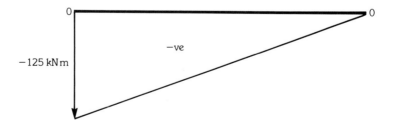

If a bending moment diagram is drawn carefully to scale, the bending moment at any point along the beam can be measured.

Structural sections

Struts, ties or beams are designed to carry the maximum load with the use of the least amount of material. (The maximum calculated load also includes a margin for unexpected stresses called a safety factor.)

The materials used to support a compressive load can have a variety of cross-sectional shapes.

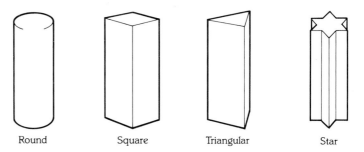

Round   Square   Triangular   Star

These can be in tubular or solid forms and made from a variety of materials.

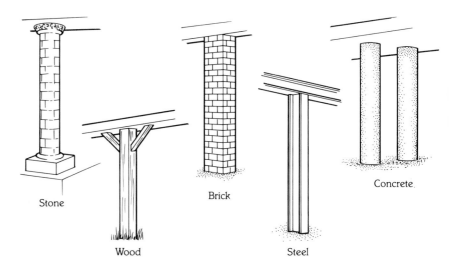

Stone   Wood   Brick   Steel   Concrete

Materials used to support tensile loads can also be made in a variety of shapes.

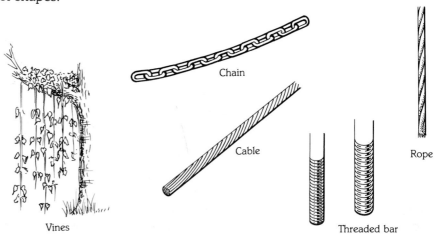

Vines   Chain   Cable   Threaded bar   Rope

Beams are subjected to both tensile and compressive forces. The performance of a material can be improved by modifying its shape.

I-shaped girder beams

The stresses in a beam are concentrated in the top and the bottom edges. The material at the sides is not useful in supporting the load.

Increasing the depth of a beam increases its resistance to bending. This can be seen on the chassis of large trailers. The beam has been cut and re-welded to increase its resistance to bending without adding to the weight.

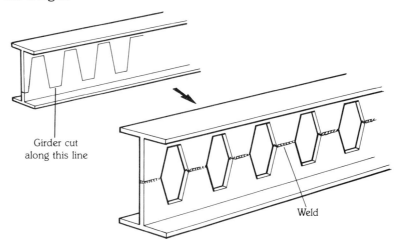

Girder cut along this line

Weld

Box girder beams

A box shape is very strong and resists bending. It can be constructed to extend across a gap to form a bridge. A box girder bridge is very strong. The traffic-way can be inside the box or on the top of the box.

A box girder bridge under construction

The advantage of an enclosed traffic-way can be appreciated when considering the effect of strong winds on high sided vehicles. The large cost of the bridge can be offset against the reduction of accidents caused by strong wind. Modern designs favour the roadway on top of the box structure. With the road on the top of the box it can be braced internally, making it stronger. Savings in materials costs can be made with this type of design when compared with other bridge designs.

Supporting structures

Guys

When a structure is anchored by stays or ropes these supporting members are called guys. They are in tension and by using three guys a very tall structure can be supported that would fall without the support given by the guys. An example of the type of structure supported by guys is a suspension bridge or radio mast.

Anchoring

This is the attachment of a guy to the ground. It is the form of attachment that allows the guy to be used to its full capability. Ropes and cables are designed to be used in tension. To avoid damaging them collet chucks are used to grip them.

Films that show the construction of suspension bridges often show the care and attention to detail required in the construction of the anchoring points. If anchorages fail the structure will fall.

Buttresses

A buttress is a type of reinforcement for a wall or pillar. The most impressive examples of this are found in Gothic architecture. This style of building used vast quantities of stone in a structure. To keep the compressive forces generated by the weight of the stone within the columns additional force had to be generated to 'push' the forces back into the structure.

Flying buttress

Flying buttresses strengthen the walls of Norwich Cathedral

This style of architecture was often designed completely in the head of the builder. It was traditionally based on his past experience of the material and the style of building. No calculations were made to check the final design prior to the start of building; the design disasters that occurred fell down and are no longer around to be seen!

Foundations

The foundations of a structure enable it to 'float' on the surface on which it stands. The sides of the foundation also 'grip' the soil around them, helping to hold the structure up. The foundations of a structure are, therefore, very important.

The shape of the foundation is important. On rock, the foundations will be dug down to the rock itself and concrete **caissons** or steel **end bearing piles** used. On soft ground or waterfront areas **friction piles** are used. Very soft soil may need a **floated foundation.**

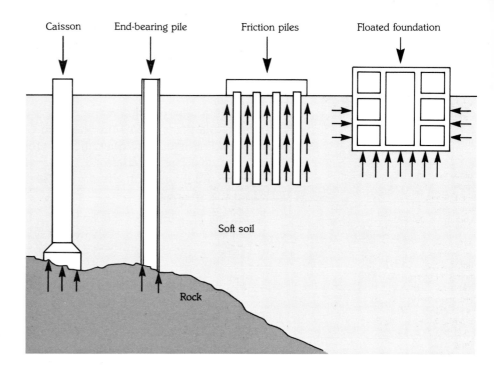

Caisson   End-bearing pile   Friction piles   Floated foundation

Soft soil

Rock

Foundations may also have to withstand an upward force, especially when used for pneumatic structures or suspension bridges. Anchorages may be drilled directly into rock or into a large concrete block buried in the ground. Temporary structures may use pegs or heavy weights to hold them down.

Localised reinforcement

Often the weakest part of a structure is where the pieces of material are joined together. Jointing techniques are complicated, especially when three or more pieces have to be joined at the same place.

There is one simple method of reinforcing that was developed during the First World War. On the wings of the wooden biplanes triangular pieces of plywood were glued to the two pieces of wood where they were joined. These pieces of plywood are called **gusset plates** and add significantly to the strength of a joint.

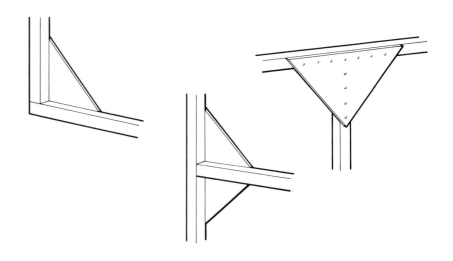

Index